FIFTH EDITION

Active Children!

Promoting Physically Active Lifestyles in Physical Education

CLAYRE K. PETRAY-ROWCLIFFE
California State University, Long Beach

Contributions by Sandy L. Blazer
Chief Academic Officer, Green Dot Public
Schools, Los Angeles, California

PEARSON

Custom
Publishing

To my family; Clay, Katie, Jed, Corrine, and Holly. I love you.
C.K.P.

To Mom and Dad. Your belief in me helped me to believe in myself.
S.L.B.

Printed in the United States of America

10 9 8 7 6 5 4 3 2

ISBN 0-536-27733-8

2006460113

CS

Please visit our web site at *www.pearsoncustom.com*

PEARSON CUSTOM PUBLISHING
75 Arlington Street, Suite 300, Boston, MA 02116
A Pearson Education Company

Dedication

This book is dedicated to:

My parents, Katie and Clay, to whom I am so grateful for their lifelong love, encouragement and support. Thank you, Mom and Dad.
P.S. Thanks, Dad, for the great photo you took of my students in 1978 that graces the back side of this book! It brings back wonderful memories...

My loving husband, Bill, with whom I have increased my capacity to live, laugh, love, and play! Go TIGER! P.S. Thanks, Bill, for your creativity and persistence in designing the cover and back side of this book!

Mama Kitten, Erika, Ryan and Kim, Tamra and Bjorn, Kristal and York, Jed, Corinne, Holly, Sierra, Vicki and Tom, Schmell, Chenell and Taylor who bring so much love and joy to my life. Thank you to my very special family!

Acknowledgments

I would like to express my gratitude to the following people who have made unique and valuable contributions to the publication of the fifth edition of this book:

Jason Dodge at Pearson Publishing for his patience and assistance with manuscript preparation.

Mr. Ben Corbett, for his computer expertise and assistance in creating the instruments and graphs in Chapter 10.

Mr. Ricardo Miranda, Ms. Patty Miranda and Mr. Kelly McWilliams for using their artistic talents to create the drawings.

The physical education specialists and classroom teachers in the ABC, Long Beach, Newport-Mesa, Tustin, and Westminster School Districts who continue to field test the activities and provide valuable feedback.

Mrs. Bonnie Carter for her outstanding writing ability, creativity, organization, and critical thinking skills that resulted in two new chapters and in improved clarity in Chapters Two through Eight.

Mrs. Tammie Dry for her writing ability, creativity and thoroughness in assisting with the reorganization of Chapters 11 to 14; these chapters now contain a much clearer presentation of concepts and activities.

Ms. Jeanette Van Metre for her organizational skills, artistic ability, and computer expertise in scanning and organizing the original artwork, improving existing pictures and creating new ones.

Dr. Emyr Williams, Mrs. June Duarte, Ms. Joyce Chino and Mrs. Krista Spina, for using this text in their university courses and providing valuable feedback.

The teachers and students at Kettering Elementary School, in Long Beach, California, for providing field experiences for the CSULB Kinesiology majors.

Mrs. Hylin Neese, elementary physical education specialist, ABC Unified School District, for mentoring the CSULB Kinesiology Majors and allowing them to observe and participate in model physical education lessons.

Mr. Chris Corliss, the Orange County Department of Education Physical Education Coordinator of Health, Sports, Fitness and Physical Education for involving me in his efforts to promote quality elementary school physical education.

Mr. John Sanders and Mr. Kurt Suhr, principals in the Newport-Mesa School District, for their strong support of physical education.

Ms. Joyce Chino, Adapted Physical Education Specialist, Long Beach Unified School District, for her passion for teaching that has energized me. Thanks also to Joyce and her students, Amy, Dilyara, Dionte, Jacob, Justin, Kai and Valerie for allowing me to take 186 pictures for the cover photo!

Mrs. Annemarie Garlin, for her wisdom, leadership, and support for quality physical education for children and for graciously writing a foreword beyond my expectations.

Dr. Sharon Guthrie, Chair of the CSULB Kinesiology Department, for her enthusiastic support of elementary school physical education coursework.

Dr. Ron Vogel, Dean, CSULB College of Health and Human Services, for his strong support of the elementary school physical education coursework.

My CSULB colleagues, Drs. Jim Davis, Michelle Magyar, Karen Hakim Butt, Grant Hill, Jeff Kress, Barry, Lavay, Ralph Rozenek, Alison Wrynn, Emyr Williams, Joyce Chino, June Duarte, Krista Spina and Hylin Neese for their professional expertise and collaboration.

Dr. Barry Lavay, for his expertise in Adapted Physical Education and for serving as a consultant in the area of special physical education for all five editions.

Dr. Mike Lacourse, former Chair of the CSULB Department of Kinesiology and current Associate Dean, CSULB College of Health and Human Services, for his outstanding leadership, professional expertise and strong support of the Elementary School Physical Education Option.

Dr. Sandy Blazer, Chief Academic Officer, Green Dot Schools (Los Angeles, CA), for her valuable contributions as co-author to the first three editions of this book. Dr. Blazer will always be a part of this book.

All the elementary school students, university students, teachers and administrators with whom I have worked over the past 32 years for their enthusiasm about physical education that has inspired me and provided extra fuel for my passion!

Foreword

Whether you have purchased this book because it is the required text in your university course, or you are currently a teacher with a desire to improve the quality of your physical education program, you have taken an important first step!

We live in an era where the media regularly focus on improved student achievement, accountability, an end to social promotion, and the possibility of rewards and sanctions for our schools. Improving education for our youth is currently foremost in the hearts and minds of parents, educators, and politicians. This is as it should be; however, sometimes the focus is narrow. A comprehensive program for students includes "best practices," in all content areas, especially in physical education. The Surgeon General has reported that "inactivity is hazardous to our nation's health." Thirty percent of youth are obese or overweight. To complicate matters, the fabric of the family is changing, and now, more than ever, society looks to our schools and our teachers to teach students to make responsible choices and to lead healthy lifestyles.

Teachers can play a vital role in promoting physical activity and fitness levels in youngsters by focusing on the needs of the "whole child." Using the information included in this book, entire staffs, or grade levels, can mobilize teams in schools and work with parent groups to provide student access to a well-planned, high quality, physical education program.

This book is an invaluable tool for educators. The format is written with busy teachers in mind. Every chapter contains practical classroom applications, complete with easy-to-follow illustrations. The author provides important information to insure that all teachers, even those who may not have felt confident in this area before, can develop a quality physical education program for students.

Preparing and planning for physical education instruction is just as important as developing lesson plans in other content areas. The benefits are numerous and your commitment to educate the mind and body is critical. Students need to be provided with physical education lessons through which they can acquire the knowledge, skills and attitudes necessary to lead physically active lifestyles.

Perhaps many of life's important lessons are learned in kindergarten; however, I suspect that many more are learned, every year, in quality physical education programs. This book provides a foundation for establishing such a quality program.

Annemarie Garlin
Principal, Loma Vista School
Tustin Unified School District
Tustin, California

Contents

Preface

WARNING

THE U.S. SURGEON GENERAL HAS DETERMINED THAT PHYSICAL INACTIVITY IS HAZARDOUS TO YOUR HEALTH!

Purpose of the Fifth Edition

Government reports and other noteworthy publications have documented the significant relationship between regular participation in physical activity and lifetime health. The lack of physical activity among Americans of all ages is so critical that it is considered a major health risk factor. Physical inactivity is associated with many diseases including stroke, heart disease, high blood pressure, osteoporosis, various cancers, Alzheimer's, depression, obesity and type 2 diabetes.

This fifth edition recognizes the importance of promoting lifetime physical activity habits in children. Physical education is the only subject area in the school curriculum that includes physical activity. The purpose of this book is to empower current and prospective teachers to develop physical education programs based upon the *National Physical Education Standards* (NASPE, 2004), that include maximal opportunity for their students to be physically active while providing the children with the knowledge, attitudes, skills and behaviors necessary to establish a physically active lifestyle. The book focuses on health related physical fitness as a foundation for regular participation in physical activity. Health related physical fitness is not an end in itself; it is a means to the end of providing students with the attributes necessary to adopt physically active lifestyles.

Intended Readers

For an elementary school physical education course, this book may be used as a primary or supplementary text. Many of the major elementary physical education textbooks have only one or two chapters that address physical activity, health related physical fitness, and obesity prevention. This book provides specific information that will assist both physical education teacher education (PETE) majors and prospective classroom teachers in establishing a physical education program aimed at promoting lifetime activity habits and minimizing the development of obesity in children.

Classroom teachers and elementary physical education specialists already out in the field will find this book useful in either supplementing existing physical education programs or in instituting new ones. This book will also be of use for administrators and parents who desire to evaluate the health related physical fitness and physically active lifestyle promotion components of elementary school physical education programs as well combat the childhood obesity epidemic.

Contents

The organization of *Active Children! Promoting Physically Active Lifestyles in Physical Education*, is designed to be clear and easy to follow. A special feature is the "Carotid Kid." Most of the book's illustrations feature this character in action!

This book is divided into five major parts. **PART ONE** (Chapters 1-3) contains information based upon extensive research on physical activity, obesity and health related physical fitness and their significant relationship to lifetime health. This fifth edition contains new content that reflects the current research and trends related to the childhood obesity epidemic and the subsequent increase in the occurrence of type 2 diabetes in children. Information presented in these chapters may be used to defend the need for establishing a physical education program aimed at promoting physically active lifestyles and preventing obesity.

PART TWO (Chapters 4-6) provides policies and procedures for implementing a quality physical education program. Chapter 4 presents the FITT guidelines and exercise principles as well as physical activity guidelines and daily steps recommendations. Chapters 5 and 6 present physical education scheduling and safety considerations, including current research on safe and dangerous exercises.

PART THREE (Chapters 7-10) focuses on the instructional process. Chapter 7 provides guidelines for writing physical education lesson plans incorporating the *National Physical Education Standards*. Chapter 8 describes how to create a classroom climate that promotes student learning. Chapters 9 and 10 focus on methods for teaching lessons that provide maximal opportunity for all students to be physically active. Chapter 9 examines how time is used in the physical education lesson and offers strategies for keeping students physically active for the majority of class time. Chapter 10 provides techniques prospective and current teachers can use to self-evaluate and reflect on their teaching, with a special focus on maximizing students' participation in physical activity.

PART FOUR (Chapters 11-16) includes physical fitness and activity concepts, written in terms that children can understand, and physical activities for developing and assessing physical fitness. Chapters 11-14 each focus on a separate component of health related physical fitness: cardiovascular fitness, body composition, muscular strength and endurance, and flexibility. Each concept, fitness exercise and activity in these chapters is broken down into simple steps that are easy for teachers to teach and children to learn. They are designed so youth experience success and feelings of competence that lead to feelings of confidence. Interwoven throughout these chapters is the importance of living a physically active lifestyle. Chapter 11, Cardiovascular Fitness, includes information on incorporating pedometers into physical education lessons. Chapter 12, Body Composition, explains the vital role of physical activity in weight control and obesity prevention. It includes the current food guide pyramid and dietary recommendations and presents a simple approach for teaching youth to read, interpret and use nutrition labels. Chapter 15 presents 20 easy-to-organize games designed to provide maximal physical activity for all children without humiliation or elimination. Chapter 16 describes procedures for making physical fitness and activity assessment a valuable learning experience that increases students' understanding of their own fitness and activity levels.

PART FIVE (Chapters 17-18) contains activities for supplementing the physical education program and promoting physically active lifestyles outside the physical education class. Chapter 17 lists practical ideas for incorporating health related physical fitness and activity concepts, not only into the physical education lesson, but into the total school curriculum. Chapter 18 provides ideas for promoting physical activity and fitness in the home and community.

The **Appendices** provide supplemental information. Appendices 1 and 2 comprise diagrams that identify the location of the body's major muscles and bones. Appendix 3 is a recommended physical education equipment list.

Information from two nationally recognized publications is integrated throughout the book: *The National Physical Education Standards* (NASPE, 2004) and *FITNESSGRAM/ACTIVITYGRAM Test Administration Manual* (CIAR, 2005). Both documents focus on implementing quality physical education programs aimed at empowering youth to adopt physically active lifestyles. The author recommends purchasing both of these books to maximize physical education curriculum development and implementation.

PART ONE

Introduction to Physical Activity and Fitness

Chapter 1, "New Definitions: Physical Activity, Exercise and Physical Fitness," defines the terms physical activity, exercise and physical fitness. Physical activity terminology and recommendations are explained. Two parts of physical fitness, skill related and health related, are defined. A rationale for health related physical fitness as a foundation for a physical education program focused on active lifestyle promotion is then presented.

Chapter 2, "A New Focus on Physical Activity," presents recent government reports, national documents and research that focus on the significant relationship between physical activity and lifetime health. The childhood obesity epidemic and subsequent increase of children with type 2 diabetes are addressed. The mission of physical education and the national physical education standards, designed to define a physically educated person, are explained.

Chapter 3, "Health Related Physical Fitness: The Foundation for a Physically Active Lifestyle," provides an in-depth explanation of each of the four health related physical fitness components: cardiovascular fitness, body composition (special focus on childhood obesity, type 2 diabetes and pre-diabetes), muscular strength and endurance and flexibility. The definition, health benefits, assessment, and achievement and maintenance of healthy levels of each component are discussed.

Chapter 1

New Definitions: Physical Activity, Exercise and Physical Fitness

The terms "physical activity," "exercise" and "physical fitness" are related; however, each term has a distinctly different definition. This chapter defines each of the three terms in light of new government documents. First, the all-encompassing term of physical activity is defined. Exercise, one type of physical activity is then clarified. The term physical fitness, and how its definition has evolved over the years, is then explained. Finally, this chapter presents a rationale for using health related physical fitness as a foundation for promoting physically active lifestyles in the physical education program.

Physical Activity

Physical activity is an umbrella term that has many parts. It is defined as "bodily movement that is produced by the contraction of skeletal muscle and that substantially increases energy expenditure (usually measured in kilocalories)." (NASPE, 2004). The Centers for Disease Control and Prevention (CDC) has established definitions for the following terms to clarify its physical activity recommendations.

♥ **Recommended physical activity.** The CDC recommendation for optimal physical activity includes both a moderate-intensity and a vigorous-intensity level. The criteria are different depending upon the intensity level; a person performing activities that meet either one of the following criteria meets the CDC physical activity recommendation.

   ♥ The **moderate-intensity** level includes activities such as brisk walking, bicycling, vacuuming, gardening or anything else that causes small increases in breathing or heart rate; these are to be performed for greater than or equal to 30 minutes per day, greater than or equal to five days per week.

   ♥ The **vigorous-intensity** level includes activities such as running, aerobics, heavy yard work, or anything else that causes large increases in breathing or heart rate; these are to be performed for greater than or equal to 20 minutes per day, greater than or equal to three days per week.

The acronym MVPA will be used throughout this book to represent moderate to vigorous physical activity. Participation in MVPA can be accomplished through lifestyle activities such as household, transportation, or leisure-time activity as well as structured exercise and physical activity training programs (see definition of exercise).

♥ **Insufficient physical activity.** Insufficient physical activity is defined as doing more than 10 minutes total per week of moderate or vigorous intensity lifestyle activities (i.e., household, transportation, or leisure-time activity), but less than the recommended level of activity (see above).

♥ **Inactivity.** Inactivity is defined as less than 10 minutes total per week of moderate or vigorous-intensity lifestyle activities including, but not limited to, household, transportation, and leisure-time activity.

♥ **Leisure-time inactivity.** Leisure-time inactivity is defined as no reported leisure-time physical activities in the previous month, including, but not limited to, any type of physical activity or exercises such as running, calisthenics, golf, gardening or walking.

Exercise

Exercise is one specific form of physical activity. It is defined as planned, structured and repetitive bodily movement done to improve or maintain one or more components of physical fitness. Exercise training and physical training are two terms that are used as synonyms for exercise.

Physical Fitness

While physical fitness has been an important objective of physical education programs for the past 125 years, there has been considerable change in the definition of physical fitness. Prior to the 1980's, the definition of physical fitness emphasized skill related fitness. In the 1980's, health related components of fitness were identified and the definition began to focus on these factors. In the late 1990's, a new, more comprehensive definition of physical fitness emerged; the new definition includes not only health related and skill related components but also physiological components.

Physical fitness is defined as a state of well-being with low risk of premature health problems and energy to participate in a variety of physical activities. It is a set of attributes that people have or achieve that relates to the ability to perform physical activity. (USDHHS, 1996) Physical fitness is a comprehensive term that includes physiological, health related and skill related components. The physiological components are beyond the scope of this book; skill related and health related fitness definitions follow.

Skill Related Physical Fitness

Skill related physical fitness consists of those components of physical fitness that are primarily important for performance in sports and of less importance to lifetime health. Skill related physical fitness is also referred to as "athletic" or "motor" fitness. One's ability in these areas, especially in reaction time and speed, is considered to be highly related to heredity; skill related fitness is more dependent on genetics and less easily improved through training. The components of skill related fitness are: 1) reaction time 2) speed, 3) power, 4) agility, 5) balance and 6) coordination (see Figure 1.1).

Figure 1.1   Skill related physical fitness components

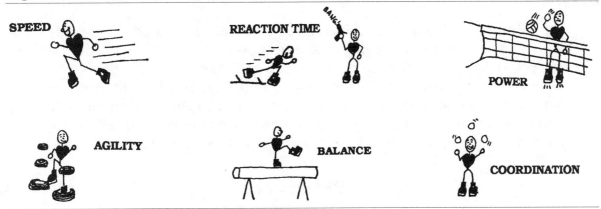

Health Related Physical Fitness

Health related physical fitness consists of those components of physical fitness that directly affect lifetime health and one's ability to regularly participate in physical activity. The health related physical fitness components are not only important for performance in sports, but are also related to lower risk of injury and illness and improved quality of life. These components are not as dependent upon heredity as are the skill related components, and therefore, have a higher potential for improvement through training. The health related fitness components (see Figure 1.2) are: 1) cardiovascular fitness, 2) body composition, 3) muscular strength and endurance and 4) flexibility (Specific information on each of the health related fitness components is contained in Chapters 3 and 11-14).

Figure 1.2   Health related physical fitness components

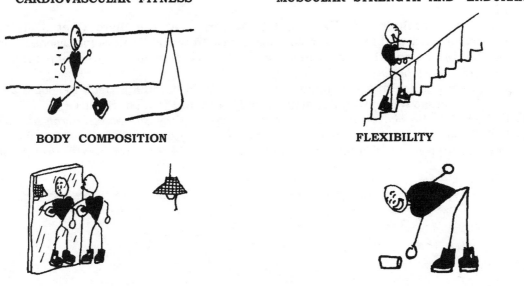

Health Related Physical Fitness as a Foundation for a Physically Active Lifestyle

It is important that both skill related and health related physical fitness activities are included in the physical education curriculum. However, since health related physical fitness components influence not only one's performance in sports, but one's ability to regularly participate in physical activity, this book focuses on a positive approach to establishing a health related physical fitness-based physical education program aimed at empowering students to establish physically active lifestyles.

References

Bouchard, C. (1993). Heredity and health related fitness. *President's Council on Physical Fitness and Sports Research Digest, 1*(4), 1-8.

Bouchard, C., Shephard, R.J., & Stephens, T. (Eds.). (1994). *Physical activity, fitness, and health.* Champaign, IL; Human Kinetics.

Cooper Institute for Aerobics Research. (2005). *FITNESSGRAM/ACTIVITYGRAM Test Administration Manual. (3rd edition). Champaign, IL*: Human Kinetics.

Corbin, C., & Lindsey, R., and Welk, G.J. (2000). *Concepts of physical fitness* (10th ed.). St. Louis: McGraw Hill.

Franks, D., Corbin, C., & Pangrazi, R. (March 2000). Definitions: Health, fitness, and physical activity. *The President's Council on Physical Fitness and Sports Research Digest, 3*(9), 1-6.

Kent, M. (1994). *The Oxford dictionary of sports science and medicine.* Oxford: Oxford University Press.

Howley, E.T., & Franks, B.D. (1997). *Health fitness instructor's guide.* Champaign, IL: Human Kinetics.

NASPE. (2004). *Physical activity for children: A statement of guidelines.* (2nd ed.). Reston, VA: NASPE Publications.

Pate, R. (1983). A new definition of youth fitness. *The Physician and Sports Medicine, 11*(4), 77-83.

Pate, R.R., Pratt, M., Blair, S.N., Haskell, W.L., Macera, C.A., Bouchard, C. et al. (1995). Physical activity and health: A recommendation from the Centers for Disease Control and Prevention and the American College of Sports Medicine. *Journal of the American Medical Association, 273,* 402-407.

U.S. Department of Health and Human Services (USDHHS). (2000). *Healthy People 2010* (2nd ed.). Washington, DC: U.S. Department of Health and Human Services.

USDHHS. (1996). *Physical Activity and Health: A Report of the Surgeon General.* Atlanta, GA: U.S. Department of Health and Human Services, Centers for Disease Control and Prevention, National Center for Chronic Disease Prevention and Health Promotion.

Chapter 2
A New Focus on Physical Activity

This chapter presents recent government reports, national documents and research that focus on the significant relationship between physical activity and lifetime health. The childhood obesity epidemic and subsequent increase of children with type 2 diabetes are addressed. The mission of physical education and the national physical education standards, designed to define a physically educated person, are explained.

The Surgeon General's Report on Physical Activity and Health

In the past, exercise for the purpose of developing physical fitness was a major goal of physical education. It was thought that out of all the outcomes of a quality physical education program, the most important influence on lifetime health was one's level of physical fitness.

In 1996, however, this narrow focus on physical fitness began to shift. The landmark federal document, *Physical Activity and Health: A Report of the Surgeon General,* concluded that Americans can substantially improve their health and quality of life by including moderate amounts of physical activity in their daily lives (USDHHS, 1996). Not since the Office of the Surgeon General's (OSG) report on the dangers of smoking, has a single government document made such a strong statement about the health of the nation. The report summarized patterns and trends and determinants of participation in physical activity.

Patterns and Trends in Physical Activity
The OSG reported the following patterns and trends in physical activity.

♥ Approximately 15 percent of U.S. adults engage regularly (three times a week for at least 20 minutes) in vigorous physical activity during leisure time.

♥ Approximately 22 percent of adults engage regularly (5 times a week for at least 30 minutes) in sustained physical activity of any intensity during leisure time.

♥ More than 60 percent of American adults are not regularly physically active.

♥ Physical inactivity is more prevalent among women than men, among blacks and Hispanics than whites, among older than younger adults, and among the less affluent than the more affluent.

♥ Nearly half of American youth 12 to 21 years of age are not vigorously active on a regular basis. Moreover, physical activity declines dramatically during adolescence.

♥ About 14 percent of young people report no recent vigorous or light-to-moderate physical activity. This indicator of inactivity is higher among females than males and among black females than white females.

♥ Participation in all types of physical activity declines strikingly as age or grade in school increases.

The findings that only a small percentage of adults are regularly active and that participation in physical activity declines as age increases raised great concern among physical education, fitness and health professionals.

WARNING

THE U.S. SURGEON GENERAL HAS DETERMINED THAT PHYSICAL INACTIVITY IS HAZARDOUS TO YOUR HEALTH!

Determinants of Participation in Physical Activity

The OSG Report also identified the following as the most influential factors on one's physical activity patterns.

♥ Competence in skills necessary to engage in regular physical activity
♥ Confidence in one's ability to engage in regular physical activity
♥ Enjoyment of physical activity
♥ Support from others
♥ Positive beliefs concerning the benefits of physical activity
♥ Lack of perceived barriers to being physically active

The identification of these key factors provides valuable information concerning the promotion of lifetime physical activity habits in elementary school physical education. The physical activities described in Chapters 11-15 are designed to develop competence and confidence, to be enjoyable and to promote positive beliefs about the benefits of physical activity.

Centers for Disease Control and Prevention Guidelines to Promote Lifelong Physical Activity Among Young People

In 1997, as a result of OSG findings, the Centers for Disease Control and Prevention (CDC) established several guidelines for school and community programs to promote lifelong physical activity among young people. The following three of these CDC guidelines involve physical education programs.

- ♥ Schools and communities should establish policies that promote enjoyable, lifelong physical activity among young people.
- ♥ Schools and communities should provide physical and social environments that encourage and enable safe and enjoyable physical activity.
- ♥ Schools should implement physical education programs that emphasize enjoyable participation in physical activity and that help students develop the knowledge, attitudes, motor skills, behavioral skills, and confidence needed to adopt and maintain physically activity lifestyles.

Both the OSG Report and the CDC guidelines implore schools to provide physical activity and health related physical fitness experiences that are enjoyable, educational, and empowering.

Physical Activity and Obesity Research

The OSG Report and the subsequent CDC Guidelines prompted government agencies and researchers to further investigate the relationship between physical activity and lifetime health. The following publications reinforce the OSG findings concerning physical activity and the urgency of implementing the CDC guidelines. Included in these publications is research, not only related to physical activity, but to the increasing occurrence of obesity, the emerging significance of the relationship between inactivity and obesity, and the link between obesity and type 2 diabetes.

- ♥ The National Youth Risk Behavior Survey (YBRS): 1991-2003 reported that the percent of high school students who attend daily physical education decreased significantly from 41.6% in 1991 to 28.4% in 2003 and that 38% of these youth watched three or more hours of TV per day on an average school day.

- ♥ Results of the Youth Media Campaign Longitudinal Survey (YMCLS), a nationally representative survey of children age 9-13 years and their parents, revealed that 61.5% of children aged 9-13 years do not participate in any organized physical activity during their non-school hours and that 22.6% do not engage in any free-time physical activity.

- ♥ The CDC reported that obesity among adults (as measured by a body mass index greater than 30) has almost doubled, increasing from 11.6 to 22% from 1990 to 2002

- ♥ Results of the 1999-2002 National Health and Nutrition Examination Survey (NHANES) indicated that an estimated 16 percent of children and adolescents ages 6-19 years are overweight. This represents a 45% increase from the overweight estimates of 11 percent obtained from NHANES III (1989-1994).

- ♥ In 2002, The CDC reported that the percent of overweight youth aged 12 to 19 (as measured by body mass index) almost tripled, increasing from five percent to 14 percent between the 1970s and 1999.

♥ The Dietary Reference Intakes Report, released by the Institute of Medicine (2002), stated that it takes an hour or more of daily physical activity to prevent weight gain and to lower cardiovascular disease risk.

♥ Dale et. al. (2002) reported that children who received physical education were more active than those who did not.

♥ In 2002, researchers (Kimm et. al) examined data from The National Heart, Lung and Blood Institute (NHLBI) Growth and Health Study in which 1,213 black girls and 1,166 white girls ages 9 to 19 were followed. They found that, by ages 18 and 19, more than 70% of black girls and 39% of white girls reported doing no regular leisure physical activity. Girls with a higher body mass index had a greater decline in physical activity.

♥ In 2003, Francine Kaufmann *(Diabesity)* reported that type 2 diabetes is increasingly being diagnosed in children, something that rarely happened 20 years ago. A sedentary lifestyle in conjunction with a consequent weight gain, is one of the major factors in the development of type 2 diabetes. More than 17 million Americans now have type 2 diabetes and these numbers are rising for all age groups and ethnicities.

♥ Researchers found that seven out of ten obese children will grow into obese adults. Most often, baby fat turns into adult fat.

♥ In 2004, researchers (K. Patrick, et. al.) reported that of seven dietary and physical activity variables examined, insufficient vigorous physical activity was the only risk factor for higher body mass index for adolescent boys and girls.

♥ In 2005, researchers (Gutin, et. al.) concluded that black and white adolescents who engaged in relatively large amounts of vigorous exercise were likely to be relatively fit and lean.

These findings provide support for expanding the focus of physical education from simply developing physical fitness to providing MVPA experiences and promoting regular participation in physical activity outside of school. A physically active lifestyle is now thought to be as, or more important, than one's level of physical fitness. Physical fitness is no longer an end in itself, a healthy level of fitness provides the foundation for regular participation in physical activity.

Assessment of Physical Activity and Health Related Physical Fitness: *FITNESSGRAM/ACTIVITYGRAM*

The significant relationship between a physically active lifestyle and health has been established. *FITNESSGRAM/ACTIVITYGRAM* (Cooper Institute for Aerobics Research, 2005) is the first national physical fitness assessment program to include a physical activity assessment for youth. *FITNESSGRAM/ACTIVITYGRAM* has identified healthy scores, known as healthy fitness zones (HFZ) for both health related physical fitness components and physical activity for males and females ages five to seventeen. The components of the *FITNESSGRAM/ACTIVITYGRAM* program are integrated throughout this book; prospective and current teachers are encouraged to purchase the *FITNESSGRAM/ACTIVITYGRAM Test Administration Manual* (see references). Chapter 3 identifies *FITNESSGRAM/ACTIVITYGRAM* assessment items for each of the health related physical fitness components. Chapter 16 presents strategies for implementing *FITNESSGRAM/ACTIVITYGRAM* that insure enjoyable, educational and empowering assessment.

Mission of Physical Education

The mission of physical education has evolved over the years. The current mission, or goal, of physical education is the result of the recent documentation on the significant relationship between regular participation in physical activity and lifetime health. The mission of physical education is (NASPE, 2004): "to develop physically educated individuals who have the knowledge, skills, and confidence to enjoy a lifetime of healthful physical activity."

The National Physical Education Standards Define a Physically Educated Person

Consistent with the new mission of physical education, The National Association of Sport and Physical Education (NASPE) (2004) has defined a physically educated person; that is, it has answered the question, "What should a student know and be able to do as a result of quality physical education instruction in grades K-12?" NASPE has identified the following six national standards for physical education.

A physically educated person:

♥ *Standard 1.* **Demonstrates competency in motor skills and movement patterns needed to perform a variety of physical activities.** The physically educated person has developed the physical skills needed to enjoy regular participation in physical activities. Elementary school physical education provides experiences through which children develop fundamental motor skills such as running, skipping, throwing and striking. Movement fundamentals provide the foundation for continued motor skill acquisition. Skills related to participating in tennis, golf, basketball, swimming, skating, skiing, dancing, walking, hiking and cycling are examples of skills that can be used to participate in lifetime activity.

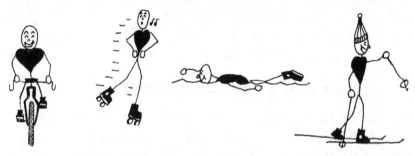

♥ *Standard 2.* **Demonstrates understanding of movement concepts, principles, strategies and tactics as they apply to the learning and performance of physical activities.** The physically educated person understands that health and wellness involve more than just being physically fit and has learned concepts from such disciplines as exercise physiology, biomechanics, and sports psychology. She recognizes the risk and safety factors associated with regular participation in physical activity. Ultimately, the physically educated person has developed sufficient knowledge and ability to independently use her knowledge to acquire new skills while continuing to refine existing ones.

♥ *Standard 3.* **Participates regularly in physical activity.** The physically educated person makes use of the skills and knowledge learned in physical education class as he regularly engages in physical activity outside of the physical education class. The physically educated person exhibits a physically active lifestyle.

♥ *Standard 4.* **Achieves and maintains a health-enhancing level of physical fitness.** The physically educated person has the knowledge, skills and willingness to accept responsibility for personal fitness, leading to an active, healthy lifestyle. For elementary school children, the emphasis is on an awareness of health related physical fitness components and having fun while participating in health-enhancing activities that promote physical fitness.

♥ *Standard 5.* **Exhibits responsible personal and social behavior that respects self and others in physical activity settings.** The physically educated person demonstrates responsible personal and social behavior in physical activity settings. He respects individual similarities and differences. Similarities and differences include characteristics of culture, ethnicity, motor performance, disabilities, physical characteristics, gender, age, race and socioeconomic status.

♥ *Standard 6.* **Values physical activity for health, enjoyment, challenge, self-expression and social interaction.** The physically educated person cherishes the feelings of confidence and competence that result from regular participation in physical activity and appreciates the benefits of a physically active lifestyle.

Summary

It is clear that regular participation in physical activity has a positive effect on lifetime health and well-being. The pervasive childhood obesity epidemic and subsequent increase in the incidence of type 2 diabetes in children further intensify the importance of promoting health related physical fitness and lifetime physical activity habits at an early age. The mission of physical education is to provide children with educational experiences that will empower them to establish health-enhancing physically active lifestyles; achieving this mission is the focus of this book.

References

Aaron, D.J., Storti, M.S., Robertson, R.J., Kriska, A.M., LaPorte, R.E. (2002). Longitudinal study of the number of choice of leisure time physical activities from mid to late adolescence. *Archives of Pediatric Adolescent Medicine, 156,* 1075-1080.

Centers for Disease Control and Prevention (CDC). (2003). Physical activity levels among children aged 9—13 years-U.S., 2002. *Morbidity and Mortality Weekly Report (MMWR),52*(33), 785-88.

CDC. (2004). Youth risk behavior surveillance—United States, 1991-2003. *MMWR,53*(SS-2), 1-100.

Cooper Institute for Aerobics Research. (2005). *FITNESSGRAM/ ACTIVITYGRAM test administration manual* (3rd ed.). Champaign, IL: Human Kinetics.

Dale, D.L., Corbin, C.B., & Dale, K. (2000). Restricting opportunities to be active during school time: Do children compensate by increasing physical activity levels after school? *Research Quarterly for Exercise and Sport, 71*(30), 240-248.

Ekelund, U., Brage, S., Franks, P.W., et al. (2005). Physical activity energy expenditure predicts progression toward the metabolic syndrome independently of aerobic fitness in middle-aged healthy Caucasians: The Medical Research Council Ely Study. *Diabetes Care, 28*:1195-1200.

Gutin, B., Yin, Z., Humphries, M. & Barbeau P. (2005). Relations of moderate and vigorous physical activity to fitness and fatness in adolescence. *American Journal of Clinical Nutrition, 81*(4), 746-750

Hedley, A.A., Ogden, C.L., Johnson, C.L., Carroll, M.D., Curtin, L.R. & Flegal, K.M. (2004). Overweight and obesity among US children, adolescents, and adults, 1999-2002. *Journal of the American Medical Association (JAMA), 291,* 2847-50.

Institute of Medicine. (2002). Dietary reference intakes for energy, carbohydrates, fiber, fat, protein and amino acids (macronutrients). Washington, DC: National Academy of Science, Institute of Medicine.

Kaufman, F.R. (2003). *Diabesity.* NY: Bantam.

Kimm, S.Y., Glynn, N.W., Kriska, A.M., *Barton, B.A., Kronsberg, S.S., Daniels, S.R., Crawford, P.B., Sabry, Z.I., & Liu, K.* (2002). Decline in physical activity in black girls and white girls during adolescence. *New England Journal of Medicine. 347,* 709-715

NASPE. (2004). *Moving into the future: National standards for physical education: A guide to content and assessment.* (2nd ed.). Reston, VA: McGraw-Hill.

NASPE. (2004). *Physical activity for children: A statement of guidelines.* Reston, VA: NASPE.

Norman, G.J., Schmid, B.A., Sallis, J.F., Calfas, K.F., & Patrick, K. (2005). Psychosocial and environmental correlates of adolescent sedentary behaviors. *Pediatrics, 116:* 908-916.

Ogden C.L., Flegal, K.M., Carroll M.D., & Johnson C.L. (2002). Prevalence and trends in overweight among US children and adolescents, 1999-2000. *JAMA, 288,* 1728-32.

Pate, R.R., Pratt, M., Blair, S.N., Haskell, W.L., Macera, C.A., Bouchard, C. et al. (1995). Physical activity and health: A recommendation from the Centers for Disease Control and Prevention and the American College of Sports Medicine. *JAMA,273,* 402-407.

Patrick, K., Norman, G., Calfas, K., Sallis, J., Zabinski, M., Rupp, J., & Cella, J. (2004). Diet, physical activity, and sedentary behaviors as risk factors for overweight in adolescence. *Archives of Pediatric Adolescent Medicine, 158,* 385-390.

Telama, R., Yang, X., Laasko, L., & Viikari, J. (1997). Physical activity in childhood and adolescence as predictor of physical activity in adulthood. *American Journal of Preventive Medicine, 13,* 317-323.

Trost, S.G., Pate, R.R., Sallis, J.F., et al. (2002). Age and gender differences in objectively measured physical activity in youth. *Medicine and Science in Sports and Exercise, 34,* 350-55.

Turley, K.R. (1997). Cardiovascular responses to exercise in children. *Journal of Sports Medicine, 24,* 241-257.

U.S. Department of Health and Human Services (USDHHS). (2000). *Healthy People 2010* (2nd ed.). Washington, DC: USDHHS.

USDHHS. (1996). *Physical activity and health: A report of the Surgeon General.* Atlanta: USDHHS.

Woo, K.S., Chook P., Yu. C.W., et al. (2004). Effects of diet and exercise on obesity-related vascular dysfunction in children. *Circulation, 109:*1981–86.

Chapter 3
Health Related Physical Fitness: The Foundation for a Physically Active Lifestyle

An optimal level of health related physical fitness provides the foundation for regular participation in health-enhancing physical activity. Chapter 1 identified the health related physical fitness components as: cardiovascular fitness, body composition, muscular strength and endurance and flexibility. Although these components are interrelated, each has distinctive features and individually contributes to one's health and ability to participate in physical activity. This chapter answers the following questions.

♥ What is the definition of each health related fitness component?
♥ What are the benefits of a healthy level of each component?
♥ How is each component assessed?
♥ What is a healthy level of each component?
♥ How is a healthy level of each component achieved and maintained?

CARDIOVASCULAR FITNESS
What is the Definition of Cardiovascular Fitness?

Cardiovascular fitness is the ability of the circulatory and respiratory systems to supply oxygen during sustained physical activity. "Cardio" means heart and "vascular" means blood vessels. Cardiovascular fitness is sometimes referred to as aerobic ("with air") or cardiorespiratory ("heart" and "lung") fitness. Activities such as walking, jogging, cycling, swimming, hiking, cross-country skiing, rowing, dancing and skating, when carried out at moderate to vigorous levels for 20 to 60 minutes, require heart and lung fitness.

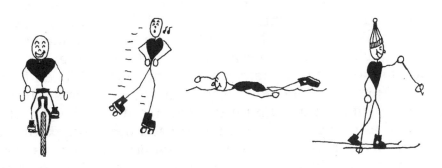

What are the Benefits of a Healthy Level of Cardiovascular Fitness?

A healthy level of cardiovascular fitness allows one to regularly participate in physical activity without undue fatigue. Cardiovascular fitness has numerous effects on one's lifetime health. It is associated with decreased risk of coronary heart disease (CHD), obesity, type 2 diabetes, high blood pressure, high cholesterol levels and some cancers.

CHD is characterized by partial or complete blockage of the coronary arteries caused by a build-up of fatty substances; CHD is responsible for 55% of the deaths in the western world. The American Heart Association has identified risk factors that increase one's risk of acquiring CHD. The risk factors fall into two categories: 1) risk factors you can't change, and 2) risk factors you can change (www.healthiergeneration.org/kids).

1.   **CHD risk factors you can't change**
♥   *Increasing age.* Over 83% of people who die of CHD are 65 or older. At older ages, women who have heart attacks are more likely than men to die from them within a few weeks.
♥   *Male gender.* Men have a greater risk of heart attack than women; men also have heart attacks earlier than women. After menopause, women's death rate from CHD increases; however, it still is not as great as men.
♥   *Heredity (including race).* Children of parents with CHD have increased risk. Heart disease risk is higher among Mexican Americans, American Indians, Native Hawaiians and some Asian Americans. This is partly due to higher rates of obesity and type 2 diabetes.

2.   **CHD risk factors you can change and the influence of physical activity on each risk factor.**
♥   *Tobacco smoke.* Smokers' risk of heart attack is two to four times greater than that of nonsmokers'. People who smoke cigars or pipes tend to have higher risk of death from CHD and stroke, but their risk is not as high as cigarette smokers'. Chronic exposure to secondhand smoke also increases one's risk of CHD.
♥   *High blood pressure.* People with high blood pressure have increased risk of CHD. High blood pressure increases the heart's workload, causing the heart to thicken and become stiffer. When high blood pressure exists with obesity, smoking, unhealthy lipid levels or type 2 diabetes, one's risk of heart attack or stroke increases several times. Regular participation in moderate-intensity physical activity has been found to decrease blood pressure. The increased heart rate during sustained physical activity (minimum 20 minutes) can result in a bigger, stronger heart muscle that pumps more blood with each beat and expand the size of the arteries. With increased arterial circumference, there is less resistance and thus reduced pressure on blood flow. Current medical guidelines recommend a blood pressure reading at or below 120/80.

♥ ***Blood lipid levels.*** One's risk of CHD increases as certain blood lipid levels increase. High triglyceride levels and unhealthy levels of "BAD" cholesterol increase risk. The definitions of the three major types of blood lipids, and their relationship to CHD follow.

   a.   *Cholesterol:* a waxy, fatty-like substance that acts as a building block for the formation of essential compounds vital to body function. Cholesterol is produced in the body and is also obtained by eating foods of animal origin. Total cholesterol values above 250 mg/dl are associated with increased CHD risk regardless of HDL cholesterol values (see definition of HDL below). Total cholesterol values below 150 mg/dl are associated with minimal CHD risk. When total cholesterol values are between 150-250 mg/dl, the total cholesterol divided by HDL ratio is more sensitive and helpful in assessing CHD risk than total cholesterol alone.

   b.   *Lipoproteins:* fat-carrying proteins in the blood
      ♥   Low-density lipoproteins (LDL's) are sometimes referred to as "BAD" cholesterol. LDL's are medium-sized proteins, high levels of which may increase one's CHD risk. An LDL level value ranging from 57-120 is desirable, the lower the value the lower the CHD risk.
      ♥   High-density lipoproteins (HDL's) are sometimes referred to as "GOOD" cholesterol. HDL's are small, protective proteins, high levels of which may decrease CHD risk. Males with HDL values greater than 45 mg/dl and females with HDL values greater than 40 mg/dl generally have less than average CHD risk.
      ♥   The total cholesterol/HDL ratio is calculated by dividing total cholesterol by the HDL value. The lower the ratio, the lower one's CHD risk. This ratio is of special significance to people with total cholesterol values between 150 and 250. Estimates of CHD risk based on this ratio are shown in Figure 3.1.

Figure 3.1   CHD risk based upon total cholesterol/HDL ratio

CHD RISK	TOTAL CHOLESTEROL/HDL RATIO	
	MALE	*FEMALE*
half average	below 3.43	below 3.27
average	3.44 - 4.97	3.28 - 4.44
twice average	4.98 - 9.55	4.45 - 7.05
thrice average	9.56 - 23.99	7.06 - 11.04

Thus, a female with a total cholesterol value of 205 and an HDL level of 103, has a CHOL/HDL ration of 1.99, and thus a *half average* risk. A female with a total cholesterol value of 205 and an HDL level of 40 has a CHOL/HDL ration of 5.1, and thus an *above average* risk.

   c.   *Triglycerides:* fat-carrying particles stored in the body, high levels (greater than 190 mg/dl) of which increase one's CHD risk.

♥   ***Obesity.*** People who have excess body fat, especially around the waist, have increased CHD risk. Carrying excess fat increases the heart's work. It also raises blood pressure, blood cholesterol (total and LDL) and triglyceride levels and lowers HDL levels. People with obesity are also at higher risk for type 2 diabetes. Physical activity can play a valuable role in reducing body fat.

♥   ***Physical inactivity.*** In 1992, the American Heart Association identified physical inactivity as a risk factor for CHD. Regular participation in physical activity (at least 30 to 60 minutes daily, depending on the activity) can also positively affect total blood cholesterol and HDL's, type 2 diabetes, blood pressure and obesity.

Two other factors that may contribute to CHD risk are individual response to stress and alcohol. People under stress may choose to overeat, smoke, or become inactive when responding to stress. Drinking too much alcohol can raise blood pressure and can contribute to high triglycerides, cancer and obesity. Although the risk CHD factors were originally identified in adults, most risk factors for heart disease have now been identified in youth.

Children are at greater risk for CHD than ever before. The number one killer of adults can no longer be considered solely a geriatric disease; it is now known that CHD is pediatric in origin. Children need to be provided with a quality physical education program that includes positive experiences aimed at developing and maintaining healthy cardiovascular fitness levels and empowering youth to establish physically active lifestyles.

How is Cardiovascular Fitness Assessed?

The PACER (Prolonged Aerobic Cardiovascular Endurance Run) is the recommended measure of cardiovascular fitness in *FITNESSGRAM/ACTIVITYGRAM* ; the one-mile run and the walk test (walk test not validated for youth under ages 13) are alternate measures. (Chapters 11 and 16 contain descriptions of the PACER.) Refer to the *FITNESSGRAM/ACTIVITYGRAM* Test Administration Manual for more specific information on the administration of the PACER as well as alternate measures of cardiovascular fitness.

What is a Healthy Level of Cardiovascular Fitness?

A healthy level of cardiovascular fitness allows the heart, lungs, and blood vessels to function efficiently in delivering oxygen and nutrients to the tissues during continuous physical activity. A high level of cardiovascular fitness is not necessary to achieve optimum health; research shows that people with a level of cardiovascular fitness in the lowest 20% of the population are at the highest risk for health problems. A person who simply achieves a level of cardiovascular fitness above the lower 20% of the population decreases his health risk substantially. *FITNESSGRAM/ACTIVITYGRAM* identifies scores on the one-mile run and PACER (Chapters 11, 16) that represent healthy levels (Healthy Fitness Zone or HFZ) of cardiovascular fitness for youth. For example, the HFZ for 11-year-old boys on the one-mile run ranges from eight minutes and 30 seconds to 11 minutes.

How is a Healthy Level of Cardiovascular Fitness Achieved and Maintained?

Healthy levels of cardiovascular fitness are achieved and maintained through participation in moderate to vigorous, physical activity (MVPA) at least four days per week. Both adults and children can participate in activities such as walking, jogging, hiking, swimming, skating, and cycling to improve cardiovascular fitness. Chapter 11 contains concepts and activities that can be incorporated into physical education lessons to develop and maintain a healthy cardiovascular fitness level and promote physically active lifestyles.

BODY COMPOSITION

What is the Definition of Body Composition?

Body composition is the amount of fat, muscle, bone, and other vital parts of the body. It is sometimes referred to as body fat and relative leanness; however, neither of these terms accurately reflects the all-encompassing term of body composition.

What are the Benefits of a Healthy Level of Body Composition?

A healthy level of body composition has numerous positive effects on one's lifetime health. Healthy body composition allows one to regularly participate in physical activity without undue fatigue. Both children and adults with healthy body composition levels are more likely to have healthier cholesterol levels, lower blood pressure, lower risk for type 2 diabetes and ultimately, decreased risk of CHD. Further, people with uncontrolled type 2 diabetes are at risk for not only CHD, but for kidney disease, blindness, and amputation.

The Effects of Obesity Upon Children. Because overweight youth are likely to become overweight adults, their lifespan is often affected. Overweight people, on average, live a decade less that those at a healthy weight. Being overweight is associated with 400,000 deaths a year.

In addition to an increased risk for physical illness, the obese child is a handicapped learner in physical education. Research shows obesity to be the fourth most important factor hampering the learning of motor skills. Physical activity is more tiring for the obese child. Chaffing of the legs may make some activities painful and create negative feelings toward these activities. As obese children enter school, they quickly become aware of how others react to them. They are often ridiculed or excluded from group membership. The self-esteem of obese children may be damaged because of the difficulty experienced in learning skills and the teasing inflicted by their peers.

Type 2 Diabetes. The childhood obesity epidemic has resulted in the diagnosis of type 2 diabetes in children. Formerly referred to as "adult-onset diabetes" because it rarely occurred in youth, type 2 diabetes is increasingly being diagnosed in children [American Diabetes Association - ADA (www.diabetes.org)]. At the time of this book's publication, an estimated 16 million Americans have type 2 diabetes and one-third, over five million, don't even know it. The Center for Disease Control and Prevention is predicting that one-third of people born in 2000 will get type 2 diabetes. People of Hispanic, African American and Native American background have a combination of genetic predisposition and higher obesity rates that put them at even greater risk. It is predicted that 53% of Hispanic women and 45% of men and 49% of African American women and 40% of men are will be diagnosed with type 2 diabetes.

Pre-Diabetes. At least 16 million Americans have a condition known as pre-diabetes in which blood glucose levels are higher than normal, but not yet high enough for the diagnoses of type 2 diabetes. A person with pre-diabetes is more likely to develop type 2 diabetes within 10 years and has an increased risk of heart attach and stroke. The ADA recommends that a person with two or more of the following risk factors be tested for pre-diabetes and type 2 diabetes:

- ♥ Overweight more than 30 pounds
- ♥ Relative (parent, brother or sister) has diabetes
- ♥ Family background is African American, American Indian, Asian American, Hispanic/Latino or Pacific Islander
- ♥ Blood pressure is 140/90 or higher
- ♥ Cholesterol (lipid) levels are not normal [HDL cholesterol (good cholesterol) is less than 40 for men or less than 50 for women and/or triglyceride level is 250 or higher
- ♥ Participates in physical activity, for at least 30 minutes, fewer than three times per week

Both pre-diabetes and type 2 diabetes may be preventable in people at risk for developing them with moderate lifestyle changes including increasing physical activity and healthier food choices. When these changes result in a 5 to 10% loss of body weight, type 2 diabetes may be eliminated.

How is Body Composition Assessed?

Body composition is assessed by determining one's percentage of body fat; two common methods of determining children's percentage of body fat are skinfold measurements and Body Mass Index (BMI).

Skinfolds. A skinfold is two thicknesses of skin and the amount of fat that lies between them. Skinfold calipers are used to take these measurements (see Figure 3.2).

Figure 3.2 Skinfold measurement

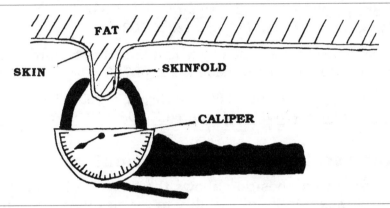

The child's **triceps** and **calf skinfolds** are measured. The triceps skinfold is taken on the back of the arm, and the calf skinfold is taken on the medial side of the calf at the point of largest circumference (Figure 3.3). All skinfolds are measured on the right side of the body.

Figure 3.3 Location of triceps and calf skinfold measurements

Triceps Skinfold   **Calf Skinfold**

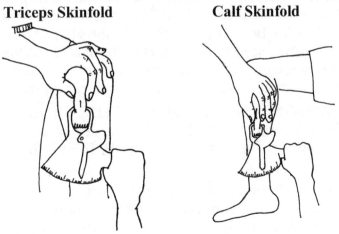

Body Mass Index (BMI). Body Mass Index is a number calculated from a person's weight and height. BMI is used as a screening tool, not a diagnostic tool; if a person has a high BMI, a direct assessment such as skinfolds must be performed to determine obesity. The calculation for BMI is shown in Figure 3.4.

Figure 3.4   Calculation of Body Mass Index

Measurement Units	Formula and Calculation
METRIC kilograms and meters	Weight(kg) / [height (m)]squared Divide weight in kilograms by height in meters squared. Since height is commonly measured in centimeters, divide height in centimeters by 100 to obtain height in meters. Example: Height = 165 cm (1.65 m), Weight = 68 kg Calculation: 68 / (1.65) squared = 24.98 or 25
ENGLISH pounds and inches	Weight (lb)/ [height (in)]squared X 703 Divide weight in pounds by height in inches squared and multiplying by a conversion factor of 703 Example: Weight = 150 lbs, Height = 5'5" (65") Calculation: [150 / (65)squared X 703 = 24.96 or 25

What is a Healthy Level of Body Composition?

A healthy level of body composition allows the heart and other organs to function optimally and maximizes one's ability to regularly participate in physical activity. The *FITNESSGRAM/ACTIVITYGRAM* (**www.fitnessgram.net**) contains standards for body composition in youth calculated from both skinfold measurements and BMI. The manual includes tables that have been adapted to indicate healthy body composition levels (Healthy Fitness Zone – HFZ) using either of these measurements.

IN FITNESSGRAM/ACTIVITYGRAM a healthy level of body composition, based upon skinfolds, is below 25% fat for boys and below 35% for girls; optimal percentages are 10 to 20% for boys and 15 to 25% for girls. Additionally, for students older than 12, *FITNESSGRAM/ACTIVITYGRAM* also identifies students with low levels of fat (boys lower than eight percent and girls lower than 14%). Students who are very lean may also have an increased health risk.

FITNESSGRAM/ACTIVITYGRAM also includes BMI HFZ for youth based upon on age and gender. For example, the BMI HFZ for an eleven-year-old girl ranges from 14 to 24. Refer to the manual for the BMI HFZ for each age and gender.

The CDC has also established BMI standards for both children and adults (**www.cdc.gov**). For children, the CDC recommends using height/weight growth charts based upon age and gender; a child whose BMI is at or above the 85th percentile is considered "at risk for overweight;" above the 95th percentile is considered "overweight." In adults, a BMI below 18.5 is classified as underweight, from 18.5 to 24.9 normal, 25 to 29.9 overweight and 30 or more obese. One limitation of BMI is that muscle weighs more than fat; thus, some individuals who have increased muscularity may have a high BMI but not have a high percentage of body fat.

How is a Healthy Level of Body Composition Achieved and Maintained?

Maintaining a healthy level of body composition is simply a daily balancing act: balancing calories consumed with calories expended for energy. Additionally, participation in moderate to vigorous activity for a continuous period of time (at least 20 minutes) will burn more fat than less vigorous, intermittent activity. Cardiovascular fitness activities not only strengthen the heart but also burn body fat; thus, the activities identified earlier that develop cardiovascular fitness may also be used to achieve and maintain a healthy level of body composition.

MUSCULAR STRENGTH AND ENDURANCE

What are the Definitions of Muscular Strength and Muscular Endurance?

Muscular strength and muscular endurance are two separate but interrelated components of health related physical fitness. Muscular strength is the largest amount of force one can put forth, through the recruitment of muscle fibers, to overcome a resistance one time. An example of strength is the maximum amount of weight a person can lift for only one repetition.

Muscular endurance is the ability to use the muscles (which are attached to the bones) many times without becoming tired. For example, swinging a tennis racket continuously while playing tennis requires endurance of the arm and shoulder girdle muscles.

What are the Benefits of a Healthy Level of Muscular Strength and Muscular Endurance?

Muscular strength and endurance have numerous effects on one's lifetime health and ability to regularly participate in physical activity. Both strength and endurance help to prevent injuries including muscle pulls and strains. The low back area is particularly susceptible to injury; strength and endurance in the muscles of both the abdominal and arm and shoulder girdle regions can reduce the incidence and severity of low back pain. Furthermore, sufficient strength helps to maintain correct body alignment.

Strength promotes bone health. Activities that develop muscular strength also make bones stronger. An increase in one's bone density (thickness) may reduce the risk of osteoporosis. People with healthy levels of muscular strength and endurance are better able to resist fatigue and more likely to regularly participate in physical activity than people with low levels of strength and endurance.

Research shows strength in relationship to body size to be the most important factor influencing how successful children are at learning motor skills. A healthy level of strength is necessary for children to be successful in learning skills with lifetime applications.

How are Muscular Strength and Muscular Endurance Assessed?

The *FITNESSGRAM/ACTIVITYGRAM* manual recommends the following items (and includes alternate measures) to assess strength and muscular endurance (see Chapter 13 for curl-ups and push-ups and Chapter 14 for trunk lift):
♥   The **Curl-up** is recommended to assess abdominal strength and endurance.
♥   The **Push-up** is recommended to assess strength and endurance of the arm and shoulder girdle region.
♥   The **Trunk Lift** is recommended to assess trunk extensor strength and flexibility.

What are Healthy Levels of Muscular Strength and Endurance?

Healthy levels of muscular strength and endurance allow one to participate in moderate to vigorous activity with minimal risk of injury. Different activities require strength and endurance of different muscle groups; for example, in-line skating involves primarily the leg muscles while swimming involves both the legs and muscles of the arm and shoulder girdle region. Adequate levels of abdominal and upper body strength and endurance are necessary to support the low back and maintain proper body alignment in most physical activities. An excessive amount of strength, as is often the goal of professional body builders, is not necessary for good health. *FITNESSGRAM/ACTIVITYGRAM* identifies scores on the curl-up, push-up and trunk lift that represent healthy levels (Healthy Fitness Zone or HFZ) of muscular strength and endurance for youth. For example, the HFZ for a 9-year-old girl on curl-ups is 9-22, for push-ups is 6-15, and for the trunk lift is 6-12 inches.

How are Healthy Levels of Muscular Strength and Endurance Achieved and Maintained?

Strength can most easily be achieved and maintained through weight training. Lifting a great amount of weight for a few repetitions is most effective for increasing strength. Research suggests, however, that until children's bones are finished growing (at approximately age 14), lifting weights may result in temporary or permanent damage to growing bones and developing muscles. Because of the possibility of injury to children, this book does not include or recommend weight lifting activities for building strength in children.

A certain amount of strength is needed, however, to develop muscular endurance. Thus, strength may be achieved and maintained through activities aimed primarily at increasing muscular endurance. Chapter 13 combines strength building activities with those for muscular endurance, wherein the student uses some or all of her body weight as the resistance.

Muscular endurance can be achieved and maintained by executing a movement with less weight (intensity) and over a longer period of time than a movement aimed at developing strength. Chapter 13 presents activities that may be used to develop endurance of the abdominal muscles and the muscles of the arm and shoulder girdle region. As stated earlier, the activities aimed at developing muscular endurance will also have some effect upon the strength of the muscles being exercised. Muscular endurance, rather than strength, is the focus of elementary school physical education.

FLEXIBILITY

What is the Definition of Flexibility?

Flexibility is the range of motion of a specific joint, or group of joints, and the corresponding muscle groups. For example, riding a bicycle requires a range of motion in the knee joint and requires flexibility of the hamstring and quadriceps muscles. A person may be quite flexible in one joint motion, but inflexible in another joint. Most physical activities require a certain amount of flexibility.

What are The Benefits of a Healthy Level of Flexibility?

Flexibility is needed for safe and effective movement. Healthy levels of flexibility in all areas of the body are needed to minimize the risk of injury during moderate to vigorous physical activities. Stretching also helps to relieve muscle cramps and may prevent muscle soreness.

How is Flexibility Assessed?

The *FITNESSGRAM/ACTIVITYGRAM* program recommends the following items to assess flexibility (see Chapter 14):

♥   The **Back-Saver Sit and Reach** measures flexibility of the hamstrings.
♥   The **Trunk Lift** measures trunk extensor strength and flexibility.

What is a Healthy Level of Flexibility?

A healthy level of flexibility is a normal level that allows one to participate in moderate to vigorous physical activity with minimal risk of injury. Very high or low levels of flexibility may represent an increased risk of injury. *FITNESSGRAM/ACTIVITYGRAM* identifies scores on the back-saver sit and reach and trunk lift that represent healthy levels (Healthy Fitness Zone of HFZ) of flexibility for youth.

How is a Healthy Level of Flexibility Achieved and Maintained?

Exercises aimed at developing flexibility stretch the muscles slowly. The length of the muscles, ligaments, and tendons partially affect the range of movement possible at each joint. Although a certain amount of flexibility is inherited, it is essential to teach children that regular participation in certain exercises can develop and maintain their flexibility. Flexibility exercises are Always performed following moderate to vigorous physical activity, regardless of whether it is continuous or intermittent. Chapter 14 presents exercises aimed at increasing flexibility of all areas of the body.

Summary

The health related physical fitness components are an integral part of a quality physical education program. These four components are the fitness components that have the greatest influence on lifetime health and on one's ability to regularly participate in physical activity for a lifetime!

References

AHA. (1992). Medical/scientific statement on exercise: benefits and recommendations for physical activity for all Americans. *Circulation, 85*(1), 2726-2730.

Blair, S.N., Clark, D.G., Cureton, K.J, & Powell, K.E. (1989) Exercise and fitness in childhood: Implications for a lifetime of health. In *Perspectives in Exercise Science and Sports Medicine: Volume 2 Youth Exercise and Sports.* C.B. Gisolfi & Lamb, D.R. (Eds.). (pp. 401-430). Indianapolis, IN: Benchmark.

Brunner, E.J. et al. (2006). Periodontal changes in children and adolescents with diabetes. *Diabetes Care, 29:* 295-299.

Bullen, B. A., Reed, R. B., & Mayer, J. (1964). Physical activity of obese and non-obese adolescent girls appraised by motion picture sampling. *American Journal of Clinical Nutrition, 14,* 211-223.

Cooper Institute for Aerobics Research. (2005). *FITNESSGRAM/ACTIVITYGRAM Test Administration Manual. (3rd edition). Champaign, IL*: Human Kinetics.

Corbin, C. B., & Pletcher, P. (1968). Diet and physical activity patterns of obese and non-obese elementary school children. *Research Quarterly, 39*(4), 460-474.

Ekelund, U. et al. (2005). Physical activity energy expenditure predicts progression toward the metabolic syndrome independently of aerobic fitness in middle-aged healthy Caucasians. *Diabetes Care, 29:* 1195-1200.

Freedman, D.A., Dietz, W.H., Srinivasan, S.R., & Berenson, G.S. (1999). The relation of overweight to cardiovascular risk factors among children and adolescents: The Bogalusa Heart Study. *Pediatrics, 103,* 1175-1182.

Furst, S. (2003). *Confessions of a couch potato.* NY: American Diabetes Association.

Gidding, S.S., Leibel, R.L., Daniels, S., Rosenbaum, M., Van Horn, L., & Marx, G.R. (1996). Understanding obesity in youth: A statement for healthcare professionals from the Committee on Atherosclerosis and Hypertension in the Young of the Council on Cardiovascular Disease in the Young and the Nutrition Committee, American Heart Association. *Circulation, 94,* 3383-3387.

Gilliam, T. B., Freedson, P. S., Geenen, D. L., & Shahraray, B. (1981). Physical activity patterns determined by heart rate monitoring in 6-7 year old children. *Medicine and Science in Sports and Exercise, 13*(1), 65-67.

Gortmaker, S.L., Dietz, W.H., Sobol, A.H., & Wehler, C.A. (1987) Increasing pediatric obesity. *U.S. American Journal of Diseases of Children. 1*:535-540.

Hedley, A.A., Ogden, C.L., Johnson, C.L., Carroll, M.D., Curtin, L.R. & Flegal, K.M. (2004). Overweight and obesity among US children, adolescents, and adults, 1999-2002. *Journal of the American Medical Association (JAMA), 291,* 2847-2850.

Lauer, R.M., Conner, W.E., Leaverton, P.E., Reiter, M.A., & Clarke, W.R. (1975). Coronary risk factors in children: The Muscatine Study. *The Journal of Pediatrics, 86*(5), 697-706.

Lee, F., Bacha, N., Gungor, S. et al. (2006). Waist circumference is an independent predictor of insulin resistance in black and white youths. *The Journal of Pediatrics, 148*(2), 188-194.

Lee, S. **et al.** (2006). Waist circumference is an independent predictor of insulin resistance in black and white youths. *Journal of Pediatrics, 148:* 188-194.

Lohman, T. (1992*). Advances in body composition.* Champaign, IL: Human Kinetics Publishers.

Newman, K. (2004). Why are we so fat? *National Geographic, 206*(2), 46-61.

Ogden C.L., Flegal, K.M., Carroll M.D., & Johnson C.L. (2002). Prevalence and trends in overweight among US children and adolescents, 1999-2000. *JAMA, 288,* 1728-32.

Pate, R., Dowda, M., & Ross, J. (1990) Associations between physical activity and physical fitness in American children. *American Journal of Diseases of Children,* 144, 1123-1129.

Patrick, K., Norman, G., Calfas, K., et al. (2004). Diet, physical activity, and sedentary behaviors as risk factors for overweight in adolescence. *Archives of Pediatric Adolescent Medicine, 158,* 385-390.

Rarick, G.L., & Dobbins, A. (1975). Basic components in the motor performances of children six to nine years of age. *Medicine and Science in Sports, 17*(2), 105-110.

Thorland, W., & Gilliam, T. (1981). Comparison of serum lipids between habitually high and low active pre-adolescent males. *Medicine and Science in Sports and Exercise, 13*(5), 316-321.

Troiano, R.P., Flegal, K.M., Kuczmarski, Campbell, S.M., & Johnson, C.L. (1995) Overweight prevalence and trends for children and adolescents. *Archives of Pediatric and Adolescent Medicine. 149:* 1085-1091.

U.S. Department of Health and Human Services (USDHHS). (1996). *Physical activity and health: A report of the Surgeon General.* Atlanta, GA: USDHHS, Centers for Disease Control and Prevention, National Center for Chronic Disease Prevention and Health Promotion.

Williams, D.P., Going, S.B., Lohman, T.G., Harsha, D.W., Webber, L.S., & Berenson, G.S. (1992). Body fatness and the risk of elevated blood pressure, total cholesterol and serum lipoprotein ratios in children and youth. *American Journal of Public Health,* 82: 358-363.

Wilmore, J.H., & McNamara, J.J. (1974). Prevalence of coronary heart disease risk factors in boys, 8 to 12 years of age. *The Journal of Pediatrics, 84*(4), 527-533.

Woo, K.S., Chook P., Yu. C.W., et al. (2004). Effects of diet and exercise on obesity-related vascular dysfunction in children. *Circulation, 109:*1981–1986.

Websites

American Diabetes Association   www.diabetes.org
American Heart Association   www.healthiergeneration.org/kids
Center for Disease Control and Prevention   www.cdc.gov
FitnessGram/ActivityGram Program   www.fitnessgram.net

PART TWO

Fitting in Fitness and Physical Activity

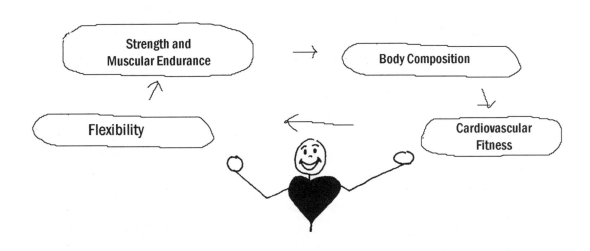

Chapter 4, "How Much Exercise and Physical Activity are Enough?" explains the FITT guidelines and principles of exercise as they relate to developing each health related fitness component. Physical activity guidelines for adults, adolescents and children are then presented. Finally, the use of pedometers and recommended daily steps for youth and adults are discussed.

Chapter 5, "Scheduling," examines considerations for scheduling physical education classes. Class size, co-educational activities, individuals with special needs, the teaching area and equipment are discussed.

Chapter 6, "A School-wide Safety Plan," presents a safety plan that includes the following components: a school health and fitness committee, student health screening, parent communication, non-participation policies, physical education clothing, potentially dangerous activities and exercises and general practices for maximizing safety.

Chapter 4

How Much Exercise and Physical Activity are Enough?

This chapter addresses two separate, yet interrelated questions.

♥ How much exercise is enough?

♥ How much physical activity is enough?

Teachers must consider the answers to both of these questions are to be considered when establishing class schedules and developing physical education lesson plans. The incorporation of this information into the physical education program helps insure that children are provided with safe and enjoyable physical education experiences in which they are physically active, able to experience the process of developing healthy physical fitness levels, and develop feelings of competence and confidence about their ability to regularly participate in physical activity. First, the FITT guidelines and principles of exercise as they relate to developing each health related fitness component are explained. Physical activity guidelines for adults, adolescents and children are then presented. Finally, the use of pedometers and recommended daily steps for youth and adults are discussed.

HOW MUCH EXERCISE IS ENOUGH?

The FITT Guidelines: Frequency, Intensity, Time and Type of Exercise

The acronym FITT stands for frequency, intensity, time and type. The definition of each FITT guideline and its specific application to each one of the health related physical fitness components based upon recommendations of the American College of Sportsmedicine (ACSM) (2000), follow.

F = Frequency. Frequency is how often or how many days per week one exercises. It is recommended that, for all components, no more than two days elapse between exercise.

♥ **Cardiovascular fitness.** Perform moderate to vigorous physical activity (MVPA) four to six days per week. Intermittent activity is recommended for children.

♥ **Body composition.** Perform MVPA four to seven days per week.

♥ **Muscular strength and endurance.** Perform muscular strength and endurance exercises two to three days per week.

♥ **Flexibility.** Perform flexibility exercises three to seven days per week, and always after MVPA.

I = Intensity. Intensity is how hard one exercises. A factor in establishing appropriate intensity is the initial fitness level of the student; intensity can be increased gradually as one's fitness level increases. Exercising too hard too soon may result in injury and frustration.

♥ **Cardiovascular fitness.** Elevate the heart rate to within the target heart rate range (see Chapter 11 – Figure 11.2) while participating in MVPA.

♥ **Body composition.** Participate in MVPA. Exercising within the Target Heart Rate Range (see Chapter 11 – Figure 11.2) is desirable, but not necessary.

♥ **Muscular strength and endurance.** Intensity is determined by the amount of weight lifted and the number of repetitions. Strength exercises are usually characterized by more weight and fewer repetitions than muscular endurance exercises. Optimal intensity is reached when one feels a slight pull in the muscles without excessive strain.

♥ **Flexibility.** Slowly stretch until mild discomfort is felt and back off slightly before holding the stretch.

T = Time. Time is the number of minutes of exercise. The optimal time of exercise depends upon one's fitness level and may be increased gradually.

♥ **Cardiovascular fitness.** Participate in MVPA for 30 to 60 minutes to achieve and maintain optimal cardiovascular fitness. A time progression for cardiovascular fitness activities conducted as part of a physical education lesson is found in Chapter 11.

♥ **Body composition.** Participate in MVPA for 30 to 60 minutes daily. Cardiovascular fitness and body composition activities are combined in the physical education lesson because of their similar frequency, intensity, time and type. The same activities that promote cardiovascular fitness also promote health levels of body composition.

♥ **Muscular strength and muscular endurance.** Strength exercises will have fewer repetitions than endurance exercises although total time exercising may be similar. Each muscular strength and endurance segment of a physical education lesson may last from three to five minutes.

♥   **Flexibility.** Perform stretching exercises for two to five minutes following MVPA. Perform four to five stretches for each major muscle group used in activity; repeat each stretch several times. Hold each stretch for 15 to 30 seconds (five to fifteen seconds with young children). Light stretching may also be performed prior to MVPA; however, only stretch muscles that have been thoroughly warmed up. Perform flexibility exercises for two to three minutes at the conclusion of the lesson.

T = Type. Type is the kind, or mode, of exercise that will develop each component. According to the principle of specificity, developing each fitness component requires a different mode of exercise.

♥   **Cardiovascular fitness.** Participate in activities that involve large muscle movements and can be performed continuously, with intermittent breaks.

♥   **Body composition.** Perform cardiovascular fitness activities, both intermittent and continuous (for short periods of time), to reduce body fat and maintain a healthy level of body composition. To maintain healthy levels of body composition, balance calories consumed and energy expended daily. To reduce body fat, expend more energy daily than calories consumed. Ultimately, participation in any type of physical activity will burn calories and positively affect body composition.

♥   **Muscular strength and endurance.** Perform activities and exercises that work the specific muscle group to be developed. The same exercises may be used to develop muscular strength and muscular endurance of a muscle group; however, strength exercises may have greater intensity (weight) and fewer repetitions (less time) than endurance exercises.

♥   **Flexibility.** Perform static exercises that stretch the muscles slowly. Avoid bouncing or jerky movements.

Principles of Exercise

Once one understands the FITT Guidelines, the principles of exercise can be applied. The FITT Guidelines and the principles of exercise are interrelated; the FITT Guidelines, in effect, clarify the principles. The five principles of exercise are:

♥   Principle of Overload
♥   Principle of Progression
♥   Principle of Specificity
♥   Principle of Regularity
♥   Principle of Individual Differences

Principle of Overload

The overload principle states that to improve a physical fitness component, one must "overload" by placing a little more stress on a muscle than it normally encounters. The overload principle is applied, by increasing the frequency, intensity or time of exercise, to each of the health related fitness components as follows.

♥ **Cardiovascular fitness.** Increase the intensity, or time of MVPA to improve cardiovascular fitness.

♥ **Body composition.** Increase the frequency or time of physical activity to achieve healthy levels of body composition.

♥ **Strength and muscular endurance.** Lift a little more weight than the muscles are accustomed to to increase strength. Increase the amount of weight lifted or the number of repetitions performed to develop muscular endurance.

♥ **Flexibility.** Stretch muscles a little bit farther each time (but not past the point of mild discomfort) to become more flexible. The frequency of stretching sessions, as well as the time each stretch is held, may also be increased. However, a higher than normal level of flexibility is not necessary, nor is it desirable.

Principle of Progression

The principle of progression states that physical fitness activities need to start slowly and increase according to one's fitness level. Incorporating the principle of progression into a physical activity and fitness program can be compared to starting a savings account. The account is opened with a small amount of money. Deposits are made little by little, and slowly the account grows. Most people do not get rich overnight. Similarly, it takes time to develop health-enhancing levels of physical fitness and activity.

Once the initial level of physical fitness and activity is determined, the intensity and time of the activities may be increased gradually. To insure regular participation, frequency remains consistent. The longer one has been inactive, the longer it will take to achieve a healthy level of fitness. It may take several months to a year to attain a healthy fitness level. Progressing too quickly may result in soreness, frustration, and even injury. Students are encouraged to progress at their own rate. The principle of progression is applied to the exercises for developing each health related fitness component as follows.

♥ **Cardiovascular fitness.** Cardiovascular fitness activities for children start out simply and in very short bouts. Chapter 11 includes a progression that begins with approximately fifteen seconds of moderate activity interspersed with fifteen seconds of rest, for a total of three minutes. Gradually the time in continuous activity increases to 75 seconds, while the resting intervals decrease to five seconds.

♥ **Body composition.** Gradually increase the time or intensity of the activity. The longer one is active, the more fat she will use for energy.

♥ **Strength and muscular endurance.** Initially, lift a portion of the body weight for five to ten seconds or approximately five to ten repetitions. Increase time or intensity gradually.

♥ **Flexibility.** Begin by holding each stretch five seconds. Progress to holding each stretch for 10 to 15 seconds.

Principle of Specificity

The principle of specificity states that specific exercises must be performed to improve each component of physical fitness. For example, push-ups develop upper body strength and muscular endurance, but have little effect upon either cardiovascular fitness or flexibility. Flexibility exercises have little effect upon any of the other components. The physical education lesson includes specific activities for developing each health related physical fitness component.

The principle of specificity also applies within the components of flexibility and strength and muscular endurance. For example, stretching exercises aimed at increasing the flexibility of the hamstring muscles have minimal effect upon the flexibility of the triceps muscles; likewise, exercises that develop the strength and muscular endurance of the upper body have little effect upon the strength and muscular endurance of the abdominal
muscles (see Figure 4.1). Therefore, in the physical education lesson, it is necessary to include a variety of exercises designed to develop strength and muscular endurance and flexibility of each specific muscle group.

Figure 4.1 **Application of the principle of specificity to flexibility and strength and muscular endurance**

Specificity in Flexibility and Muscular Strength and Endurance

Flexibility

Triceps Flexibility Exercise

Hamstring Flexibility Exercise

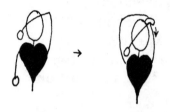

Muscular Strength and Endurance

Upper Body Strength and Endurance Exercise

Abdominal Strength and Endurance Exercise

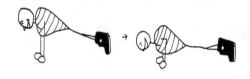

Principle of Regularity

Children need to regularly participate regularly in health related physical fitness activities to achieve healthy physical fitness levels. A minimal requirement for most components is three to four days per week. The information presented under FITT Guidelines pertaining to frequency of exercise provides optimal requirements for regularity for each health related fitness component.

Principle of Individual Differences

Every person is unique due to differences in genetic make-up, health, nutrition, body fat, and motivation. Do not compare children to each other; encourage each child to progress at her own rate and to achieve a fitness level within the Healthy Fitness Zone (Chapter 16). It is helpful if teachers who have developed optimal fitness levels empathize with those students who have never participated in physical fitness activities. If teachers have been inactive for some time, they may, through participation in the physical education activities, improve along with the students. Everyone can improve in health related physical fitness!

HOW MUCH PHYSICAL ACTIVITY IS ENOUGH?

The previous section on health related physical fitness explained the FITT guidelines and principles of exercise as they apply to achieving and maintaining a healthy level of each fitness component. Because regular participation in moderate to vigorous physical activity (MVPA) is now known to be as, or more important that ones' fitness level, new research (Corbin & LeMasurier, 2002) has identified physical activity guidelines for adults, adolescents and children.

Physical Activity Recommendations For Adults

Two publications provide physical activity guidelines for adults. The Surgeon General's Report on Physical Activity (USDHHS, 1996) includes physical activity recommendations for adults focused on increasing physical activity of sedentary individuals. The Institute of Medicine (2002) published guidelines for adults aimed at weight management.

Surgeon General's Report on Physical Activity

The Office of the Surgeon General (OSG) reported that people of all ages, both male and female, benefit from regular participation in moderate amounts of physical activity. The OSG report established two levels in its physical activity recommendation.

Level 1. All American adults should accumulate at least 30 minutes of moderate physical activity equivalent to brisk walking on most, if not all, days of the week. Figure 4.2 lists some examples of activities and minimal participation times considered equivalent to 30 minutes of brisk walking.

Figure 4.2 Examples of moderate activity

Examples of Activities Expending 150 Calories	
Washing and waxing a car for 45-60 minutes	Raking leaves for 30 minutes
Washing windows or floors for 45-60 minutes	Walking 2 miles in 30 minutes
Playing touch football for 30 to 45 minutes	Swimming laps for 20 minutes
Playing volleyball for 45 minutes	Wheelchair basketball for 20 minutes
Gardening for 30-45 minutes	Basketball (playing a game) for 15-20
Wheeling self in wheelchair for 30-40minutes	Bicycling 4 miles in 15 minutes
Walking 1¾ miles in 35 minutes (20 min/mile)	Jumping rope for 15 minutes
Basketball (shooting baskets) for 30 minutes	Running 1½ miles in 15 minutes
Bicycling 5 miles in 30 minutes	Shoveling snow for 15 minutes
Dancing fast (social) for 30 minutes	Stair walking for 15 minutes
Pushing a stroller 1½ miles in 30 minutes	

Level 2. The Report stated that people who already include moderate physical activity in their daily lives can see additional health and fitness improvement if they increase the duration of their moderate activity and/or include vigorous (increased intensity) activities three to five days per week.

Ultimately, the primary focus of the OSG Report was to help the greatest number of people, especially sedentary individuals, to achieve the greatest health benefits.

Institute of Medicine of the National Academies of Science

In 2002, the Institute of Medicine (IOM) published the following statement concerning physical activity recommendations focused on nutrition and weight management (IOM, p. 697).

> Thirty minutes per day of regular activity is insufficient to maintain body weight in adults in the recommended body mass range from 18.5 to 24 and achieve all the identified health benefits fully. Hence, to prevent weight gain as well as to accrue additional, weight-independent health benefits of physical activity, 60 minutes of daily moderate intensity physical activity (walking or jogging at 4 to 5 mph) is recommended....As both lack of physical activity and obesity are now recognized as risk factors for several chronic diseases, logic requires that activity recommendations accompany dietary recommendations.

The OSG and IOM recommendations have different intentions, and are thus, different. While the OSG focused on the general population and recommendations geared to promoting physical activity for its value to overall health, especially for the sedentary individual, the IOM recommendation focused on physical activity and nutrition as they relate to weight management. Thus, a sedentary person can receive substantial health benefits through regular participation in 30 minutes of moderate physical activity; whereas a person desiring to maintain a healthy body weight may need to increase to 60 minutes and consider dietary habits.

Physical Activity Guidelines For Adolescents

The previous guidelines were developed for adults. In 1994, an international consensus conference developed physical activity guidelines for adolescents (Sallis, Patrick & Long, 1994) (see Figure 4.3). The recommendations, similar to the OSG adult guidelines, include both moderate and vigorous physical activity.

Figure 4.3 Physical activity guidelines for youth aged 13 to 18

Physical Activity Guidelines for Adolescents
1. All adolescents should be physically active daily, or nearly every day, for at least 30 minutes as part of play, games, sports, work, transportation, recreation, physical education or planned exercise, in the context of family, school and community activities.
2. Adolescents should engage in three or more sessions per week of activities that last 20 minutes or more and that require moderate to vigorous levels of exertion.

Physical Activity Guidelines for Children

Children have different developmental needs and abilities than adolescents and adults. Children need activity for normal growth and development, need time in physical activity to develop lifetime physical activity skills and need to focus on building all parts of health-related physical fitness. Thus, the National Association for Sport and Physical Education (NASPE, 2004) published guidelines concerning appropriate amounts of physical activity specifically for preadolescent youth (see Figure 4.4).

Figure 4.4   Physical activity guidelines for children aged 5 to 12

Physical Activity Guidelines for Children

1. Children should accumulate at least 60 minutes, and up to several hours, of age-appropriate physical activity on most if not all days of the week. This daily accumulation should include moderate and vigorous physical activity with the majority of the time being spent in activity that is intermittent in nature.

2. Children should participate in several bouts of physical activity lasting 15 minutes or more each day.

3. Children should participate each day in a variety of age appropriate physical activities designed to achieve optimal health, wellness, fitness, and performance benefits.

4. Extended periods of inactivity (periods of two or more hours) are discouraged for children, especially during the daytime hours.

Elementary school physical education lessons can provide children with some of these necessary physical activity experiences. Including a variety of age appropriate activities, some of which consist of 15 minutes or more of moderate to vigorous activity interspersed with brief periods of rest, will help children meet the activity guidelines. Through the physical education curriculum, children and parents can be educated about the guidelines to insure that children regularly participate in the recommended physical activities.

Daily Step Recommendations

Another daily physical activity recommendation involves measuring the number of steps one takes. Research investigating the relationship between number of steps taken daily and overall health is ongoing; however, some initial recommendations have been made (see chapter 11 for a description on the use of pedometers to measure steps) for adults and youth.

♥ *Adult Step Recommendation.* Experts recommend approximately 10,000 steps daily for adults.

♥ *Youth Step Recommendations.* Experts differ on the recommended daily steps for youth. The President's Council on Physical Fitness and Sports (PCPFS) offer the President's Active Lifestyle Award (PALA) for youth who accumulate at least 13,000 (males) or 11,000 (females) steps per day for six consecutive weeks (PCPFS, 2003). Other research indicates that these step requirements may be slightly higher to maintain a healthy body mass index.

These initial step recommendations will most likely be revised as more research data is generated. At this time, they provide the best guidelines available and can be used to motivate and empower both youth and adults.

Summary

Answering the question, "How much exercise is enough?", involves understanding the FITT guidelines and principles of exercise. Answering the question, "How much physical activity is enough?", involves understanding the purpose and benefits of physical activity in relationship to overall health and well-being, cardiovascular disease and weight control.

Physical education is the only subject in the school curriculum that involves movement; thus, physical education classes are the only lessons in school during which children can be physically active while learning about the value of health related physical fitness and regular participation in physical activity! Incorporating the exercise and physical activity guidelines into each lesson, as well as the total curriculum, will insure that children have physical fitness and activity experiences that are safe, educational and fun!

References

American College of Sportsmedicine (ACSM). (2000). *ACSM's Guidelines for Exercise Testing and Prescription.* (6th ed.). Philadelphia: Lippincott, Williams & Wilkins.

American Heart Association. (1992). Medical/scientific statement on exercise: Benefits and recommendations for physical activity for all Americans. *Circulation, 85*(1), 2726-2730.

COPEC. (1992). *Developmentally appropriate physical education practices for children: A position statement of the Council on Physical Education for Children.* Reston, VA: NASPE.

Franks, B.D., Corbin, C., & Pangrazi, B. (2000). Definitions: Health, fitness, and physical activity. *President's Council on Physical Fitness and Sports Research Digest, 8*(1), 1-6.

Hellmich, N. (1999-6/29). Journey to better fitness starts with 10,000 steps. *USA Today,* p. 1.

IOM. (2002). *Dietary reference intakes for energy, carbohydrates, fiber, fat, protein and amino acids (macronutrients): National Academy of Sciences, IOM.* Washington, DC: IOM.

Knudson, D.V., Magnesson, P., & McHugh, M. (2000). Current issues in flexibility fitness. *President's Council on Physical Fitness and Sports Research Digest, 3*(10), 1-6.

NASPE. (2005). *Moving into the future: National standards for physical education: A guide to content and assessment.* St. Louis, MO: Mosby.

NASPE. (2004). *Physical activity for children: A statement of guidelines.* (2nd ed.). Reston, VA: NASPE Publications.

Pangrazi, R., Beighle, R., & Sidman, C. (2003). *Pedometer power.* Champaign, IL: Human Kinetics.

Pate, R.R., & Hohn, R.C. (Eds.). (1994). A contemporary mission for physical education. In *Health and fitness through physical education,* Champaign, IL: Human Kinetics.

Pate, R., Pratt, M., Blair, S., Haskell, W., Macera, C., Bouchard, C. et al. (1995). Physical activity and health: A recommendation from the CDC and the American College of Sports Medicine. *Journal of the American Medical Association. 273,* 402-407.

President's Council on Physical Fitness and Sports (PCPFS). (2003). *The President's Challenge Physical Activity and Physical Fitness Awards Program.* Bloomington, IN: PCPFS, USDHHS.

Sallis, J., Patrick, K., & Long, B. (1994). An overview of international consensus conference on physical activity guidelines for adolescents. *Pediatric Exercise Science, 6,* 299-301.

Tudor-Locke, C. (2002). Taking steps towards increased physical activity: Using pedometers to measure and motivate. PCPFS *Research Digest, 3*(17).

Tudor-Locke, C., & Myers, A.M. ((2001). Methodological considerations for researchers and practitioners using pedometers to measure physical activity. *RQES, 72*(1), 1-12.

USDHHS. (1996). *Physical activity and health: A report of the Surgeon General.* Atlanta, GA: USDHHS, CDC, National Center for Chronic Disease Prevention and Health Promotion.

Vincent, S., Pangrazi, R., Raustrop, A., Michaud Tomson, L., & Cuddihy, T. (2004). Activity levels and BMI of children in the United States, Sweden, and Australia. Medicine and Science in Sports and Exercise, *35*(8), 1367-1373.

Chapter 5
Scheduling

Like any other subject in the curriculum, physical education must be planned for and carefully scheduled throughout the school year so that students receive optimal benefits from each lesson. Accordingly, the primary focus of this chapter is on the following scheduling considerations:

- ♥ The Daily Class Schedule
- ♥ Class Size
- ♥ Co-Educational Classes
- ♥ Students with Special Needs
- ♥ The Teaching Area
- ♥ Equipment

The Daily Class Schedule

A prearranged physical education schedule needs to be established for each classroom. Daily physical education is optimal; however, physical education should be taught a minimum of three days per week for 30 to 45 minutes. Benefits from the program will be minimal if classes meet less frequently or for a shorter period of time. If only physical fitness activities are taught on certain days, a 20-minute period may be adequate. However, the practice of teaching physical fitness without any time devoted to skill development, and the other objectives of the program, is discouraged.

When a physical education schedule is established for an entire school, it is suggested that five-minute breaks are scheduled between classes. This is particularly important when back-to-back classes are taught by the same teacher or use the same equipment or teaching area.

Class Size

No more than one classroom, or a 35 student maximum, is taught at one time. Teachers are not asked to teach reading, math, and science to more than one classroom; nor should they be asked to teach physical education to more than one classroom. When a physical education class contains over 35 students, a dangerous environment is created; the teacher is unable to insure that each student performs the movements safely and correctly. Additionally, the more students there are in a class, the more difficult it is to give the students specific feedback regarding their individual progress. Inevitably, in an overcrowded class, the amount of teaching diminishes and the primary concern of the teacher becomes class control rather than quality instruction.

Co-educational Activities

Physical education activities at all levels, especially in the elementary school, are co-educational. Until puberty, girls are, at any given age, usually ahead of boys in growth and maturation. With proper training and equal opportunities for participation, girls have the potential for the development of equal or greater strength than boys. Co-educational classes provide experiences for girls in which they can participate on an equal basis with boys. This is an opportune time for the girls to gain confidence in their physical abilities and develop positive self-esteem. Boys, as well as girls, benefit when activities are coeducational. The purpose of Title IX is to guarantee males and females equal opportunity for participation in all activities.

Individuals With Special Needs

When establishing a physical education schedule, all children must be provided with developmentally appropriate physical education experiences. Some students may have special needs that limit their participation in certain activities.

Public Law 105-17: Individuals With Disabilities Act (IDEA)

The Individuals With Disabilities Act (IDEA) of 1990 is a major piece of legislation that defines and outlines the federal government's commitment to the education of all individuals with disabilities. This law mandates the inclusion of physical education as part of special education, and defines children with disabilities as those children with:

♥ Mental retardation

♥ Hearing impairments including deafness, speech or language impairments

♥ Visual impairments including blindness

♥ Serious emotional disturbance

♥ Orthopedic impairments

♥ Autism

♥ Traumatic brain injury

♥ Other health impairments: limited strength, vitality, or alertness, due to chronic or acute health problems such as a heart condition, tuberculosis, rheumatic fever, nephritis, asthma, sickle cell anemia, hemophilia, epilepsy, lead poisoning, leukemia, or diabetes

♥ Specific learning disabilities

The Least Restrictive Environment

The intent of the law is to provide full educational opportunities for all children with disabilities in the "least restrictive environment." The schools are to provide opportunities for participation in physical education activities ranging from a regular physical education class to a special adapted physical education class. The following scheduling options may be considered:

1. **Students are included in regular physical education classes.**
   Students with disabilities participate, within their capabilities, in physical education activities with non-disabled peers. They may participate in all of the activities, or may attend classes on a limited basis, depending upon their abilities. The following are suggestions for including students with disabilities in physical education activities:

♥ A student with a visual impairment jogs with a sighted student who is wearing a bell on a belt.

♥ Students who are unable to run, walk while others jog.

♥ Flags, hand signals, or other visual cues are used with students with hearing-impairments to designate starting and stopping.

♥ Directions are simplified using drawings and other audio-visual cues.

♥ Stations are used at which the students work at their own rate.

♥ A Peer Tutor or Cross-aged Tutor Program in which fifth or sixth grade students serve as teaching assistants for students with disabilities is implemented.

♥ Physical fitness assessment of non-disabled students is modified for certain disabled students. Alternate items are administered when appropriate.

2. **Separate adapted physical education classes are established for individuals with special needs.** Adapted Physical Education has been defined by Lavay in 1997 as:

> A sub-discipline of physical education, designed to meet the unique needs of individuals with movement difficulties who cannot safely and successfully participate in regular physical education. Adapted physical education is educationally movement based, designed to assist in the total development of the individual in the physical, cognitive and affective domains. It is a specialized program tailored to enable each student to reach his optimum potential while developing a positive attitude and lifetime interests toward physical activity.

Some elementary schools employ an adapted physical education specialist, a teacher with a degree in physical education and a specialization in adapted physical education, whose job is to work primarily with children identified with disabilities. Separate programs are maintained only if it is in the best interests of the students. The ultimate goal is to help each student attain a level of competency that will allow him to be transferred to the least restrictive environment.

The intent of PL 105-17 is to insure the placement of the disabled student in the most educationally beneficial environment. Each student is to be placed in the setting that allows him to best meet with success.

The Teaching Area

A teaching area for health related physical fitness is designated. Many teachers assume that an outdoor area is most desirable for conducting physical fitness activities. Most physical education specialists, however, recognize that to teach structured physical fitness activities and concepts, an indoor area provides an environment more conducive to learning. The ability of a teacher to conduct an effective lesson outdoors is often limited by distractions.

If a cafeteria, multi-purpose room, or other large indoor area is available, every effort should be made to reserve this area for physical fitness instruction. An indoor area has the benefit of less outside noise, and classes are held regardless of weather conditions. Physical fitness instruction involves not only moving, but also the learning of fitness concepts. Just as math is not taught out on the playground, neither should it be assumed that physical fitness activities are best taught outdoors.

If an outdoor area is used to teach physical fitness activities, certain precautions are taken to maximize student learning and insure the students' safety. Blacktop surfaces need to be smooth, without cracks, and free of gravel and dangerous objects. Grassy areas need to be level, free of holes, and checked on a regular basis for broken glass and other dangerous objects. Additionally, the teaching area is to be as free of distraction as possible. Physical fitness activities are not scheduled while other students are out at recess.

Establishing the schedule and designating a teaching area require cooperation between teachers and administrators. Without communication within the school, and support from the principal, it is difficult to conduct an effective physical education program.

Boundaries

Specific boundaries need to be established within the teaching area; they are to be large enough to allow the students to perform activities without bumping into each other. Plastic cones can be used to designate a large square or rectangular activity area. Six to eight cones are adequate for grades four through six; however, grades kindergarten through three require more. If plastic cones are not available, other items such as trash cans, and students' lunch pails or backpacks are used.

Lunch pails for boundaries   **Cones for boundaries**

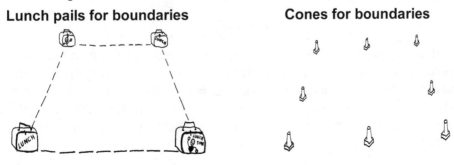

Equipment

Extensive, expensive equipment is not required to conduct health-related physical fitness activities. Most of the activities included in Part Four of this book can be taught with minimal equipment; however, equipment offers the teacher a greater selection of activities and may increase student motivation. The following minimal equipment is suggested to help to add structure and variety to the activities.

1. **Cones for Boundaries.** Six to twenty plastic cones mark boundaries.

2. **Portable CD Player with Remote.** A battery operated, portable CD player may be used to play music. Student ideas for music may be solicited; playing students' favorite songs (screen songs before playing!) makes the activity more fun! A remote frees the teacher to circulate among the students.

3. **Mats, Carpet Squares, or Towels.** Carpet squares are useful for flexibility and strength and muscular endurance exercises performed on the ground. Students can bring large towels from home if mats are unavailable. Although towels do not provide cushioning, they protect students' hands and clothes.

When using pedometers, or teaching skills using jump ropes, basketball, and hula hoops, one piece of equipment is needed for each child. Educators are not asked to teach reading and math without textbooks; therefore, they should not be asked to teach physical education without equipment. Just as one math book is purchased for each child, so should one pedometer, jump rope, basketball and hula hoop be purchased for each child. The PTO or similar group may be approached for equipment funding. A suggested equipment list for a quality program is included in Appendix B.

Summary

A prearranged physical education schedule, designated teaching area and adequate equipment are necessary to insure a quality physical education program. Children's special needs are considered so that every student can be provided with developmentally appropriate physical activities. Each child must be provided with the opportunity to successfully participate in all physical education activities.

References

Auxter, D., Pyfer, J., & Huetting, C. (2004). *Principals and methods of adapted physical education and recreation.* (10th ed.). St. Louis: C. V. Mosby.

Block, M. (1994*). Including students with disabilities into regular physical education.* Baltimore, MD: H. Brooks Publishing.

Eichstaedt, C. B. & Lavay, B. (1992). *Physical activity for persons with mental retardation: Infant to adult.* Champaign, IL: Human Kinetics.

Eichstaedt, C.B. & Kalakian, L.H. (1993*). Developmental/Adapted physical education: Making ability count* (3rd ed.). New York, NY: MacMillan.

Hellison, D. (2003). *Teaching responsibility through physical activity.* Champaign, IL: Human Kinetics.

Horvat, M. Eichstaedt, C. B., Kalakian, L. H., & Croce, R (2003). *Developmental/Adapted physical education: Making ability count.* (4th ed.).San Francisco: Benjamin Cummings

Jansma, P. & French, R. (2001). *Special physical education* (3rd. ed.). Englewood Cliffs, NJ: Prentice-Hall.

Kelly, L. (1995). (Ed.). *Adapted physical education national standards.* Champaign, IL: Human Kinetics.

Lavay, B. (2005). *Adapted physical education: A resource guide for professionals and students.* Long Beach, CA: CSULB.

Lieberman, L. J. & Houstan-Wilson, C. (2002). *Strategies for inclusion: A handbook for physical educators.* Champaign, Ill: Human Kinetics.

Office of Handicapped Individuals. (1977). *White House conference on handicapped individuals.* Washington, D.C.: Government Printing Office.

Petray, C., Freesemann, K., & Lavay, B. (1997). Understanding students with diabetes. *Journal of Physical Education, Recreation & Dance, 68*(1), 57-62.

Rouse P. (2004). *Adapted games and activities.* Champaign IL: Human Kinetics.

Seaman, J. (1995). (Ed). *Physical BEST and individuals with disabilities.* Reston VA: American Alliance for Health, Physical Education, Recreation and Dance.

Seaman, J. A., DePauw, K. P., Morton, K. B., & Omoto, K. (2003). *Making connections: From theory to practice in adapted physical education.* Scottsdale AZ: Holcomb Hathaway.

Sherrill, C. (2004). *Adapted physical activity, recreation and sport: Crossdisciplinary and lifespan.* (6th ed.). Dubuque, Iowa: WCB McGraw-Hill.

Sherrill, C. (2004). *Adapted physical activity, recreation and sport: Crossdisciplinary and lifespan.* (6th ed.). Dubuque, Iowa: WCB McGraw-Hill.

Winnick, J. P. (2005). *Adapted physical education and sport.* (4th. ed.). Champaign Ill., Human Kinetics.

Winnick, J. P. & Short, F. X. (1998). *The Brockport health related physical fitness test.* Champaign, IL: Human Kinetics.

Chapter 6
A School-wide Safety Plan

Students receive many benefits from participation in health related physical fitness-based activities; however, participation in moderate to vigorous physical activity can increase one's risk of injury. To insure students' experiences are safe and enjoyable, a school-wide safety plan is established. This chapter presents a safety plan that includes the following components: a School Health and Fitness Committee, student health screening, parent communication, non-participation policies, proper physical education clothing, potentially dangerous exercises, and general practices for maximizing safety.

School Health and Fitness Committee

A School Health and Fitness Committee is established to provide support and guidance for the physical education program. This committee consists of four to eight people; members may include the school nurse, the principal, a primary-grade teacher, an intermediate-grade teacher, a PTA member, the school psychologist, parents, and student representatives. It is helpful if the parents on the committee are employed in a health or fitness-related profession. When a classroom teacher attempts to implement a health related physical fitness-based program for his class alone, he can organize a similar committee on a smaller scale. Again, the principal, school nurse, parents, and students are included. The committee may be given a name related to the school mascot. For example, the Loma Vista Cougars might have the "Cougars for Health and Fitness."

The purpose of the School Health and Fitness Committee is to involve a variety of school personnel, students, and parents in establishing guidelines for the physical education program. Some of the committee's responsibilities are to (see Chapter 18 for ideas):

- Formulate a letter to parents (Figure 6.1) advising them of the program.
- Establish safety guidelines for the school or classroom.
- Obtain films, guest speakers, and special demonstrations related to health related physical fitness and physical activity

♥ Organize fund-raising events to promote physical fitness and finance the purchase of new equipment for the program.

♥ Edit a monthly newsletter to educate parents about the value of physical activity and reinforce the importance of a physically active lifestyle.

♥ Develop a physical activity and fitness booklet to be sent home to parents.

The benefits of a School Health and Fitness Committee are numerous. The more people within the school and community involved in supporting and guiding the physical education program, the greater its chances for success.

Student Health Screening

Children are not allowed to participate in health related physical fitness activities without some type of health screening. The Committee on School Health of the American Academy of Pediatrics has issued a position statement regarding health and physical exams for students. The position statement emphasizes the necessity for minimal health screening for all students. The school nurse or other qualified individual screens each child and checks medical records to determine each student's health status. If any uncertainty exists regarding a child's physical limitations, parents are consulted.

Physical Education Clothing

Students are encouraged to wear clothing appropriate for moderate to vigorous physical activity; communication with parents (Figure 6.1) helps to insure children are dressed properly. Loose clothing and some type of athletic shoes are most suitable. The instructor makes the final decision as to whether or not a child is dressed appropriately for activity. Elementary school-age children do not require shower facilities to participate in physical education activities.

Parent Communication

A letter to parents, similar to the one shown in Figure 6.1, is sent home before starting the physical education program. The letter supplements the screening process by requesting that parents call the school nurse or child's teacher concerning their child's health limitations. Additionally, the letter may contain a health status information section that the parent fills out concerning his child. The letter explains the importance of participation in regular physical activity and informs parents of their child's physical education class schedule. The letter can also publicize a *Physical Activity Night* (Chapter 18) held to inform parents and students of the program. Videotapes, slides, and guest speakers are used to explain the importance of physical activity to growing children. Nutrition and healthy food choices can also be discussed. Communicating with parents about the program and involving them in health screening encourages parental support of and involvement in the program.

Figure 6.1 Letter to Parents

September 25, 2008

Dear Parents:

Tustin Ranch School is proud to announce the start of a new **health related physical fitness-based** physical education program. The mission of the program is to help students develop positive physical activity habits that will carry over into adulthood. Did you know:

- The percentage of overweight children and adolescents has doubled in the last 30 years and that 20 to 30% of children are obese?
- Only tobacco contributes to more deaths than diet and physical inactivity?
- Diet and physical inactivity are related to a variety of chronic conditions including heart disease, cancer, stroke, type 2 diabetes, hypertension, and osteoporosis?
- Nearly half of American youth 12 to 21 years of age are not vigorously active on a regular basis. Moreover, physical activity declines dramatically during adolescence?
- Participation in all types of physical activity declines strikingly as age or grade in school increases?

The faculty at Tustin Ranch School is concerned about these statistics. We will be teaching activities and concepts aimed at helping students to: develop a love for activity, feel good about themselves and their physical abilities, achieve and maintain healthy levels of physical fitness, and ultimately, develop positive physical activity habits outside the school setting.

Your child's physical education class will be held on Monday, Wednesday, and Friday from 9:00 to 9:45 A.M. We are asking for your help in seeing that he/she is dressed in clothing and shoes suitable for moderate to vigorous physical activity on these days. We would also like to know if you are aware of any physical condition that could affect your child's participation in physical activity. Please call the school nurse or your child's classroom teacher with any pertinent information.

We are excited about our new mission to promote physically active lifestyles. You are invited to attend **Family Physical Activity Night** to find out more about our program and the importance of physical activity for your child. It will be held on Tuesday, October 17, from 7:00 to 8:00 P.M. in the multi-purpose room. Please come dressed for activity and ready to have some fun!

Please call me if you have any questions. I look forward to seeing you on October 17 at 7:00 P.M.!

Sincerely,

Mrs. Annemarie Garlin
Annemarie Garlin, Principal

Non-participation Policies

Once each child's health status is determined, a procedure for handling non-participation excuses is established. Students and parents are then informed of their responsibilities.

1. **Obtain a Note From Parents.** Students are required to bring a note from parents to be excused from physical education activities.

2. **Obtain the School Nurse's Approval.** The school nurse approves non-participation notes at the beginning of the school day; students are encouraged to get the nurse's approval before school starts. If a school nurse is not available on physical education days, students are asked to give notes to the classroom teacher or physical education specialist at the start of the school day. Arrangements for non-participating students are made early in the day so physical education time is not wasted.

3. **Removal from Class.** A non-participating student is not allowed to sit on the side and watch the class as she may distract participating students. Arrangements are made for her to be in the library or another classroom during the lesson.

4. **Complete a Writing Assignment.** Non-participating students complete a writing assignment related to health related physical fitness and physical activity during physical education class time.

5. **Restriction from Recess.** Students who are excused from physical education are also restricted during recess periods. This policy discourages excuses aimed solely at avoiding physical education. Implementing and enforcing non-participation policies consistently sends a message to students and parents that physical education is a valued subject area and not just optional free play. A program that includes an enthusiastic teacher and enjoyable activities in which all children are active and successful, encourages maximum participation of all students.

Potentially Dangerous Activities and Exercises

Researchers have determined that certain movements have the potential to cause for injury in both children and adults. The physical education teacher needs to be aware of these exercises and avoid any exercise that is potentially dangerous. Experts have identified the following activities and exercises as having the potential to cause injury.

Muscular Strength and Endurance Exercises Performed Quickly. Quick, jerky movements use momentum instead of strength. Effective strengthening requires controlled movement, up and down against gravity. Examples of exercises traditionally performed using fast and jerky movements are timed sit-ups and push-ups. In most cases, it is not safe to time students while performing exercises. This creates a dangerous emphasis on speed rather than proper performance of the exercise.

Ballistic Stretching. Bouncing or jerking movements using any part of the body are to be avoided. Muscle strains and pulls may result from stretching a muscle too far by a quick or jerking movement. Examples of ballistic stretching include: toe touches, waist twists, cherry pickers, belly slappers, windmills, and arm circles/swings.

High Impact Activities. Performing jumping or bouncing movements may increase one's risk of hip, knee, ankle and foot injury. Landing on one foot repeatedly and bouncing in the same spot are of particular concern.

Standing Quadriceps/Hip Flexor Stretch. This stretch, in which one holds the ankle with the same hand and pulls the leg back and to the side, puts the bent knee at risk for injury. A safer alternative is to use the opposite hand to hold the ankle and pull the leg straight back.

Double Leg Lift. This exercise, in which one lies on his back and lifts and lowers both legs while they are straight, causes the back to arch and puts pressure on the spine.

Sit-up. Several aspects of the sit-up may cause low back or neck injury. A full sit-up, with bent or straight legs, may cause low-back injury. Holding the feet during a sit-up has the same danger. Placing hands behind the head may put stress on the neck. Timed sit-ups use momentum instead of strength. A curl-up or "crunch," (legs are bent to 140 degrees and not held) in which one places the arms along side the body, and curls up only until the shoulders are off the floor, is a safe alternative (see Chapter 13).

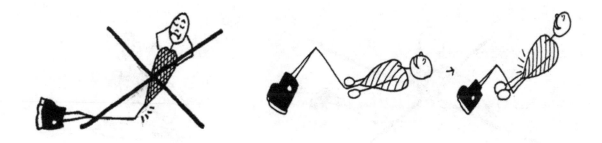

Back Bend and Bridging. Back bends and bridging (performed by wrestlers and football players to strengthen the neck) involve extreme back hyperextension and may cause injury to the neck and back. Arching the vertebrae in the back or the neck puts individuals into a position in which they can easily and permanently injure their discs. A safe alternative is a trunk lift, during which one lifts the trunk off the floor in a slow and controlled manner to a maximum height of 12 inches (see Chapter 14).

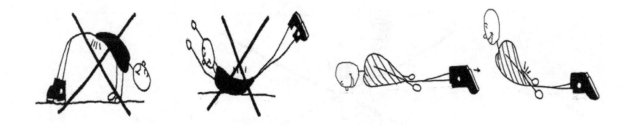

The Deep Knee Bend, Squat, and Duck Walk. These exercises may be damaging to the knee joint. Over-bending that occurs during these activities stretches ligaments and progressively weakens the bindings of the joint. Children (and adults) should not squat so low that the angle of the knees is less than 90 degrees. A safe alternative is a half-squat during which the angle of the knee is greater than 90 degrees.

The Hurdler Stretch. Leaning either forward or backward in the hurdler position may put pressure on the knee, low back, and hip and groin area. A safe alternative is the reverse hurdler stretch (see Chapter 14).

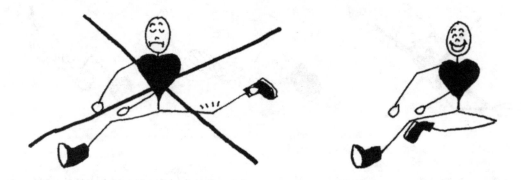

Inverted Bicycle and Plough. The inverted bicycle, in which one lies on the floor, lifts the legs back over the head, and moves the legs in a pedaling motion, places undue pressure on the spine and the neck. The Plough, in which one extends the legs overhead and backwards behind the head and neck, has similar dangers.

Locking the Knees. Locking the knee joint during any movement may strain the surrounding ligaments and cartilage. This puts pressure on the knees and low back and can cause the bones to misalign. When reaching forward from either a sitting or standing position, bend the knees slightly (avoid locked knees). Bend from the hips, not the waist, and maintain a straight back.

Rotating the Neck Backward. Rotating the head forward and backward may put pressure on the neck. The head can be tilted slowly from side to side, but not rotated backward. Avoid any uncontrolled rotation movements of the neck and spine.

Landing on the Balls of the Feet. Constant running or bouncing on the balls of the feet during cardiovascular fitness activities may result in injury. Students are instructed, when running, to land heel to toe, and when jumping up and down, to absorb the force by utilizing the entire foot and bending the knees.

General Practices For Maximizing Safety

The following are general practices for maximizing safety. Teachers and other school personnel work together to insure that these practices are followed.

♥ **Avoid using the "NO PAIN--NO GAIN" approach.** Encourage children to push past the first signs of tiring; however, also teach them the difference between initial fatigue and pain that may result in injury.

♥ **Vary activities.** Use a wide variety of exercises and opportunities for physical activity to minimize the chances for injury (and boredom!).

♥ **Avoid dangerous environmental conditions.** Do not perform vigorous activity outdoors in excessive heat or humidity or when the air quality is at a dangerous level. Exercise caution when temperatures are above 82 degrees F (28 C).

♥ **Look for danger signals during and following activity.** Some of these danger signals are: 1) breathlessness that persists long after exercise, 2) bluing of lips that is not due to cold or dampness, 3) pale, clammy skin or cold sweating during or following activity, 4) unusual fatigue, 5) persistent shakiness after exercise, and 6) muscle twitching.

♥ **Allow children to run a maximum of one-half mile (800 meters) in competition and three miles (5K) for recreation.** Children are not to run a distance greater than one-half mile (800 meters) in competition. The American Academy of Pediatrics recommends, in non-competitive situations, that children do not run a distance greater than three miles.

♥ **Adhere to the principles of exercise.** Incorporate the FITT guidelines and the principles of exercise into the program (see Chapter 4).

♥ **Avoid implementing weight training programs for youth under age 14.** Weight training, especially a focus on strength development, puts children's bones and muscles at risk for injury. Muscular endurance exercises, performed with high repetitions and low weight are recommended.

Summary

Children need to be provided with enjoyable, injury-free physical education lessons! Implementing a school-wide safety plan will provide a learning environment in which all children can learn and participate safely.

References

Andersen, R.E., Crespo, C.J., Bartlett, S.J., Cheskin, L.J., & Pratt, M. (1998). Relationship of physical activity and television watching with body weight and level of fatness among children: NHANES III. *JAMA, 279,* 938-942.

Corbin. C.B., & Pangrazi, R.P. (1998). *Physical activity guidelines: Appropriate physical activity for children.* Reston, VA: National Association for Sport and Physical Education.

Liemohn, W., Haydu, T., & Phillips, D. (1999). Questionable exercises. *President's Council on Physical Activity and Fitness Research Digest, 7*(4), 1-7.

Lubell, A. (1989). Potentially dangerous exercises: Are they harmful to all? *Physician and Sports Medicine, 17*(1), 187-192.

Mohnsen, B. (2005). Legal risks and opportunities: Dangerous exercises. *CAHPERD Journal, Spring,* 25-26.

Thorndyke, M.A. (1996). A brief look at contraindicated exercises. *Strength Conditioning, 18*(4), 31-32.

PART THREE

The Instructional Process

Chapter 7, "**Lesson Planning**," provides a detailed lesson plan format for planning and teaching physical education lessons based on the National Physical Education Standards. Behavioral objectives, safety precautions, preparation, methods and organization, concepts, instructional cues, transitions and homework are included.

Chapter 8, "**Creating a Classroom Climate that Promotes Student Learning**," presents the following topics that influence the classroom climate: standards for behavior, feedback and motivational strategies.

Chapter 9, "**Organizing Class Time to Maximize Students' Physical Activity in Physical Education**," defines the time-use categories of Activity, Instruction, and Management (AIM) time and explains how to plan for effective use of class time in the physical education lesson. Instructional strategies for optimizing each AIM category are presented.

Chapter 10, "**Self-Evaluating and Reflecting on the Teaching Process**," provides strategies for teachers to use in self-evaluating their lessons and monitoring their progress in the following areas: teacher movement, teacher demonstrations, student demonstrations, names, inappropriate and overused words and phrases, feedback, use of class time.

Chapter 7
Lesson Planning

Developing optimal levels of health related physical fitness and promoting regular participation in physical activity is an ongoing process. Activities that promote the development of physical fitness and the enjoyment of participation in physical activity cannot be included in some lessons and ignored in others; if maximal benefits are to be achieved, students need to participate in physical fitness activities a minimum of three days per week. This chapter first provides a format and minimum time allotments for teaching the health related physical fitness components. An approach for planning a quality physical education lesson, based upon the national physical education standards (NASPE, 2004), is then presented.

Format for Teaching Health Related Fitness

Figure 7.1 shows a suggested format and minimum time allotments for teaching activities to develop each health related fitness component. A moderate to vigorous warm-up is held first for two to five minutes. The warm-up insures that there is adequate blood flow to the muscles before specific exercises are performed. A few general flexibility stretches may follow the warm-up; only muscles thoroughly warmed up are stretched. Cardiovascular fitness activities, which also affect body composition, are then held for five to twelve (longer if possible) minutes. Muscular strength and endurance activities for the arm and shoulder girdle and abdominal regions follow for three to five minutes. Flexibility exercises aimed at stretching the major muscle groups used during activity, are performed at the conclusion of the lesson for two to three minutes.

Figure 7.1 Sequence and time allotments for teaching health related fitness

FITNESS COMPONENT	TIME IN MINUTES
1. Moderate to Vigorous Warm-up	2 to 5
2. Optional Flexibility	1
3. Cardiovascular Fitness and Body Composition	5 to 15
4. Muscular Strength and Endurance (may be performed before or after cardiovascular fitness activities)	3 to 5
5. Flexibility Cool Down	2 to 3

Fitting in Fitness

Specific time allotments for health related physical fitness activities are dependent upon the scheduling of physical education classes (Chapter 6). A classroom teacher may have more freedom in scheduling physical education for his own class than a physical education specialist who is responsible for scheduling physical education for all classes in the school.

Physical education lessons generally last from 20 to 45 minutes. In 30 to 45 minute lessons, there is adequate time to teach health related physical fitness activities along with skills such as individual/lifetime sports, team sports, rhythms, dance, gymnastics, aquatics, and outdoor recreation. When physical education classes are scheduled for only 20 minutes, it is difficult to include both health related fitness and skill activities in a single lesson. One possible alternative, when limited to a 20-minute class period, is to teach primarily health related physical fitness activities three days per week (it is always fun to end the lesson with an active game—see Chapter 15), and teach skill activities on alternating days (see Figure 7.2). When teaching skills on alternating days, these activities can be organized to maximize student participation and thus positively affect cardiovascular fitness.

Figure 7.2 Alternating the teaching of physical fitness and skills

20 MINUTE PHYSICAL EDUCATION CLASSES--
5 DAYS PER WEEK

Monday	Tuesday	Wednesday	Thursday	Friday
Fitness	Skill	Fitness	Skill	Fitness

In some situations, it is difficult to include health related physical fitness activities in lessons three days per week; when this is not possible, homework assignments can be given through which students participate in activity outside the school setting. Assigning physical activity homework encourages students to make regular participation in physical activity a part of their lives outside the school setting.

The Physical Education Lesson Plan

Teaching health related physical fitness activities requires pre-planning. Figure 7.3 shows a sample health related physical fitness lesson plan that is appropriate for students with low fitness and activity levels and limited fitness knowledge.

Figure 7.3 Sample health related physical fitness lesson plan

Teacher: Jodi Parker   **Date:** 2/14/2008   **Lesson length:** 20 min.

(minutes)

Major activities to be taught	Health Related Physical Fitness Activities 　Warm-up 　Strength and endurance of upper body and abdominal muscles 　Low Impact Rhythmic Aerobics (cardiovascular fitness and body 　　composition 　Flexibility/cool down
Grade level:	Fourth　　**Number of Students:**　　　　　　32

Type and quantity of equipment	carpet squares (1 per student, 1 for teacher, 4 time-out squares)	37
	compact disc (cd) or tape player	1
	pre-recorded music (songs for warm-up, upper body, abdominals, cardiovascular fitness/body composition and cool-down/flexibility)	5 songs
	cones for boundaries	8
	concept sign (flashcard) – On one side: "What happens to the heart when we are active?" On the other side: "It beats faster and gets stronger."	1
	muscle signs: hamstrings, quadriceps, gastrocnemius, deltoid, triceps, abdominals	6

Safety precautions	Encourage students to participate at their own level. Caution students to avoid jerking and bouncing and to modify a movement if they have pain, especially in their neck or low back.

Behavioral Objectives to Meet The National Physical Education Standards (1, 2, 3, 4, 5, 6)	
Motor	The students will perform non-stop movement, marching if they get tired, during low impact aerobics. **(Standards 1, 3, 4)**
Cognitive	The students will state that the heart muscle beats faster and gets stronger with activity when asked during low impact aerobics and at the end of the lesson. **(Standard 2)**
Affective	The students will give high fives to at least five other students while participating in low impact rhythmic aerobics. **(Standards 5, 6)**

Preparation	1. Pre-record music: make a music tape for the aerobics section with 10 seconds of music alternating with 10 seconds of silence.
	2. Secure one carpet square for each student and 4 extra for time-out areas.
	3. Create a rules (**a.** Listen, **b.** Respect Others, **c.** Hands and Feet to Yourself) and consequences (**a.** Warning, **b.** Student Time-Out, **c.** Teacher Time-Out) sign.
	4. Create a flash card sign for concept. On one side – "What happens to the heart when we are physically active?" On the other side – "It beats faster and gets stronger."
	5. Create flash card sign for muscles with the scientific name on one side and location on the other: hamstrings, quadriceps, gastrocnemius, deltoid, triceps, and abdominals.
	6. For curl-ups, put a masking tape line across the width of each carpet, four inches from one end of the carpet.
	7. Set up 8 cones in a 30' x 30' square for classroom boundaries.
	8. Place rules and consequences sign within view of all students.
	9. Scatter carpet squares (one for each student) two to three feet apart inside the classroom boundaries.
	10. Place four carpet squares outside the boundaries for time-out areas.
	11. Place the cd player outside the classroom boundaries.
	12. Place concept flashcards beside cd player

Skills/Activities/ Topics and Allotted Time	Methods and Organization Include Skill Progressions and Diagrams	Instructional Cues, Skill Modifications and Concepts
| **Diagram of formation for entire lesson** | ```
              T /   Tape Player
      0        0              0
         X /   X /    X /   X /
      X /  X /   X /  X /   X /
T / 0  X /   X   X /  X /   X / 0 T /
      X /    X /    X /  X /
       X /        X /  X /          Key
      X /   X /  X /  X /       0- boundary cone
         X /    X /   X /          X- student
      0         0          0    /- carpet square
              T /                 T/ -time out area
``` | |
Review rules and Consequences	Post rules and consequences sign so all students can see it.	Enforce rules and consequences consistently
A. Students pair up with the person closest to them.		**A.** "Raise your hand if you do not have a partner."
B. Students explain the rules and consequences to each other.	**B.** One student explains the rules to the other. The other student then explains the consequences for choosing not to follow the rules.	**B.** "If you get a time-out it's not because I don't like you, it's because I don't like what you are doing."
C. Review location of time-out areas		
```

Health Related Physical Fitness	Health Related Physical Fitness	Health Related Physical Fitness
	Music in background One carpet square per child Teacher models and participates Use student demonstrations Use positive specific feedback Most instructions are given while students are active Teacher circulates among students Use a scatter formation Each student goes at own rate and is responsible for her own fitness	
Activity #1 **Warm-up** 2 - 5 minutes Movements around and over carpet squares **A.** Walk around **B.** Jog around **1.** Change direction **2.** Clap hands **C.** Jump over **D.** Skip around **E.** Gallop around - (Change lead leg) **F.** Slide around - changing direction **Optional Flexibility** 1 minute Hold each stretch for 5 to15 seconds	**Activity #1** **Warm-up** **A.** Put hand over heart--feel heart rate before starting.." Teacher models **B.** Take pulse in between activities. . **C.** Swing arms **E.** Use both legs to lead **Optional Flexibility**	**Activity #1** **Warm-up** **A.** "Is your heart beating fast or slow?" **B.** "Is the heart beating faster? Yes, it's beating faster and getting stronger." **Optional Flexibility** (Chapter 14).
Transition 10 - 15 seconds	"When I say 'heart muscle,' how quickly can you stand up and hold your arms out to the side? Heart muscle!"	
Activity #2 **Muscular Strength and Endurance** 3 - 5 minutes **A. Arm and Shoulder Girdle Region-**2 to 3 min. (5 to 20 seconds of each exercise)	**Activity #2** **Muscular Strength and Endurance** **A.** Keep back straight--do not let abdomen sag or gluteus maximus stick up in the air. Pull belly button into the spine.	**Activity #2** **Muscular Strength and Endurance** (Chapter 13) **A.** Modify a movement if you feel pain in neck or low back.

1. Flat tire 2. Bent-knee push-up 3. Push-up Measures upper body strength and endurance	1. Start in bent-knee push-up position. Back is straight, hands under shoulders, fingers pointing forward. Lower the body to the floor keeping the back straight. Rest the body on the floor. Push back up. 2. Same as #1 except you push back up without touching the floor. Keep the back straight. 3. Start in the up position, knees off the floor, Lower the body so that the elbows are at a 90-degree angle. Push up to the starting position.	1. "Keep your gluteus down!" 2. "How many can you do in 5 seconds?" 3. "Backs straight"
Transition 10 - 15 seconds	"Now let's make our stomach muscles stronger. Please sit on your carpet with your knees bent and soles the feet on the floor."	
B. Abdominal Region **1. Sit-backs and assisted sit-ups** **2. Sit and hold** **3. Curl-up** Measures strength and endurance of the abdominal muscles	**B.** Pull with abdominal muscles—avoid jerking or bouncing 1. Sit on carpet with knees bent. Slowly lean back and lower yourself to the floor. Slowly sit up by using hands on the back of the legs. 2. Place arms at side, palms down. Curl up slowly until the shoulder blades are just off the floor and hold this position. Hold for 5 seconds. Curl back down slowly. 3. Lie on back with knees at a 140 degree angle, feet on the floor. Place arms at side, palms down. Line up fingertips with the edge of the masking tape. Curl up until fingers reach the edge of the carpet.. Curl back down--head touches the carpet..	**B.** "Pull belly button into spine." 1. "Go back slowly, count to four." "Can you sit up without holding your legs?" 2. "Pull belly button in." 3. "Don't sit all the way up - stop when fingertips reach the edge of the carpet." "Pull your belly button in."
Transition 10 - 15 seconds	"When I say faster, how quickly can you carpet square and put your hand over your heart? "Faster!"	
Activity #3 **Cardiovascular Fitness and Body Composition** 5 to 15 minutes	**Activity #3** **Cardiovascular Fitness/Body Composition** Feel pulse before beginning Make an aerobic cd alternating 10 seconds of music with 10 to 15 seconds of silence during which students feel their pulse and concepts are taught.	**Activity #3** **Cardiovascular Fitness and Body Composition** (Chapters 11, 12) High or low impact-- student choice

Rhythmic Aerobic Exercise	Rhythmic Aerobic Exercise	Rhythmic Aerobic Exercise
A. March in place	**A.** Stop and feel pulse after 10 seconds.	**A.** "Is your heart beating faster?"
B. March in different directions	**B.** Stop and feel pulse after 10 seconds.	**B.** "That's right, our heart beats faster with activity."
C. Step side to side	**C.** Stop and feel pulse after 10 seconds.	**C.** "When our heart beats faster, it gets stronger."
D. Add a clap	**D.** Stop and feel pulse after 10 seconds.	
E. Grapevine step	**E.** Take pulse	
F. Movements around carpet		
G. ???????????	**G.** Use student ideas and student demonstrations	
Transition 10 - 15 seconds	"When I say 'Stronger' how quickly can you walk slowly around your carpet square? 'Stronger!'"	
Flexibility Cool Down 2 - 3 min.	**Flexibility Cool Down** Play slow, relaxing music in the background	**Flexibility Cool Down** (Chapter 14)
1. Hold each stretch for 5 to15 seconds	**1.** Stretch the shoulder, arm, back, leg and stomach muscles used in the lesson.	
A. Neck rotation	**A.** Rotate neck from side to side-- look to the left then to the right. Gently pull chin down toward chest. If neck hurts, change the movement."	**A.** "Don't rotate neck backward"
B. Triceps and Deltoid stretch	**B.** Bring right arm across body, palm facing toward body. Place left hand above right elbow and pull left arm toward body. Change arms.	**B.** "Deltoid muscles are in the shoulder, triceps are in the back of the arm."
C. Gastrocnemius stretch (calf stretch)	**C.** Stand with one leg forward, one leg back. Toes are pointed straight ahead. Bend front knee, keep back heel down. Keep torso upright.	**C.** "If you do not feel the stretch in the calf, move your legs further apart."
D. Back saver sit and reach	**D.** Sitting on carpet square, stretch both legs out in front. Bend right leg and place the sole of right foot on the floor. Extend arms forward and stretch toward toes. Hold for one to two seconds. Repeat on other side.	**D.** The sit and reach measures hamstring flexibility; the muscles in the back of our legs.
E. Trunk lift	**E.** Lie face down carpet, arms at side, palms up. Lift chest slowly off the floor a few inches at a time. Hold chest up at highest point. Slowly lower chest back to carpet.	**E.** This exercise measures how strong and flexible our trunk is.
2. Closure/ Homework	**2.** Ask someone at home, or the school principal, what happens to your heart rate when you are active?	**2.** It beats faster and becomes stronger.

The physical education lesson plan contains the following major components: equipment, safety precautions, behavioral objectives, preparation, activities, methods and organization, instructional cues and concepts, transitions, and homework. Each of these items plays an important role in implementing the lesson.

Equipment

The teacher identifies the equipment (including quantity) necessary to teach the lesson. The equipment in the sample lesson plan consists of eight cones, 37 carpet squares, the rules and consequences sign, signs for concept and muscles, compact disc player and pre-recorded music.

Safety Precautions

Safety precautions pertain to exercising safely, proper use of equipment and any other areas that affect the safety of the students. Safety precautions play a key role in preventing accidents and injuries and are also important for liability purposes. In the sample lesson plan, the safety precautions focus on injury prevention.

Behavioral Objectives

Specific objectives identifying desirable student behavioral outcomes are written for each physical education lesson; as with the other areas of the curriculum, each of the three domains of learning is addressed. The behavioral objectives are aimed at meeting the National Physical Education Standards (NASPE, 2004) (see Chapter 2). Traditionally, the motor domain has been given more attention than the other two domains; however, the cognitive and affective domains are equally important. Cognitive objectives are necessary for the student to understand the "what's, why's and how's" of health related physical fitness and physical activity and are the focus of Standard 2. Affective objectives which can be the most difficult to measure, focus on the students' personal and social behavior (Standard 5) and values (Standard 6). If a student does not enjoy the physical fitness activities, nor feel good about himself as a result of having participated in them, he will be less likely to value physical fitness and incorporate regular physical activity habits into his lifestyle. Of course the motor objectives play a key role in providing students with opportunities to develop movement competency (Standard 1), participate in physical activity (Standard 3) and achieve physical fitness (Standard 4). All three domains of learning are of equal importance and are included in each lesson. Each of the six standards is included in the sample lesson plan. The motor objective focuses on the students' continuous participation in physical activity (Standards 1, 3, 4), the cognitive objective focuses on knowledge about the heart's response to moderate to vigorous physical activity (Standard 2), and the affective objective is aimed at interacting with peers in a respectful manner (Standard 5) and making the lesson an enjoyable and social experience (Standard 6).

Preparation

The teacher lists the steps necessary to organize and prepare the teaching area ahead of time. In the sample lesson, preparation includes: pre-recording music, creating rules and concepts signs, placing masking tape on carpet squares, setting up boundaries, and scattering carpet squares and placing four of them outside the boundaries for time-out areas.

The Three Columns of the Lesson Plan

The heart of the lesson plan is organized into three vertical columns. Activities are listed in the first column, methods and organization are listed in the second, and instructional cues, skill modifications, and fitness concepts are listed in the third column. Chapters 11-14 include activities and concepts for each health related physical fitness component and Chapter 15 contains games that can be used when developing a lesson plan.

Activities. The activities column in the sample lesson includes exercises and activities that warm-up the body, develop muscular strength and endurance, develop cardiovascular fitness and body composition, and stretch the muscles used in the lesson. The warm-up is held first. This may consist of an active game or locomotor movement activity as described in the lesson plan. Flexibility exercises may be included prior to muscular strength and endurance and cardiovascular fitness activities; however, muscle groups must be warmed up before they are stretched. It is now thought that the most important time to stretch the muscles is following moderate to vigorous activity; thus flexibility exercises are always performed at the conclusion of the lesson to stretch the specific muscle groups used in the lesson.

Activities are listed in progression from easiest to most difficult within each area. For example, under strength and endurance of the muscles of the arm and shoulder girdle region, the exercises progress sequentially. A flat tire, during which the student is in a push-up position and lowers his body to the floor, is performed first. The next exercise is a bent knee push-up; this is slightly more difficult because the chest does not rest on the floor in between each push-up. The third exercise is a regular push-up; the level of difficulty increases because the knees do not rest on the floor. (Chapter 13 contains a description of each of these exercises.)

When activities are taught in progression, students are more likely to perform them successfully and thus, develop positive attitudes toward physical activity. Successful participation also promotes the development of feelings of competence that lead to confidence. Moreover, when more difficult activities are eventually introduced to challenge students, those children who are not capable of performing them may continue to practice the easier movements. Teaching activities in progression from easy to more difficult will minimize student frustration, discouragement, behavior problems, and negative attitudes toward physical activity.

Methods and Organization

The Methods and Organization column consists of instructions concerning skills and skill modifications, exercise and activity modifications, organizational techniques, strategies for increasing teaching effectiveness and diagrams. Most of the information in the methods and organization column of the lesson plan in Figure 7.3, consists of instructions for performing exercises; this is typical of a beginning level health related physical fitness lesson plan.

When the information in the methods column refers to one or more specific activities in the first column, the activities and methods are located directly across from one another and numbered correspondingly. For example, as shown in Figure 7.4, number one in the methods column provides the proper form for number one (flat tire) in the activities column. Thus, when performing a flat tire, the back is straight, hands are under shoulders and fingers are pointing forward. Similarly, the method labeled number two refers to the bent knee push-up, and number three refers to the push-up.

Figure 7.4 The interrelationship of the three lesson plan columns

Skills/Activities/ Topics and Allotted Time	Methods and Organization Include Skill Progressions and Diagrams	Instructional Cues, Skill Modifications and Concepts
Activity #2 Muscular Strength and Endurance 2 - 3 minutes **A. Arm and Shoulder Girdle Region** 1 to 2 min. (5 to 20 seconds of each exercise)	**Activity #2 Muscular Strength and Endurance** A. Keep back straight--do not let abdomen sag or gluteus maximus stick up in the air. Pull belly button into the spine.	**Activity #2 Muscular Strength and Endurance** Modify a movement if you feel pain in your neck or low back
1. Flat tire	1. Start in bent-knee push-up position. Back is straight, hands under shoulders, fingers pointing forward. Lower the body to the floor keeping the back straight. Rest the body on the floor. Push back up.	1. "Keep your gluteus down"
2. Bent-knee push-up	2. Same as #1 except you push back up without touching the floor. Keep the back straight.	2. "How many can you do in 5 seconds?"
3. Push-up Measures upper body strength and endurance	3. Start in the up position, knees off the floor, Lower the body so that the elbows are at a 90 degree angle. Push back up to the starting position.	3. "Keep back straight"

Instructional Cues, Skill Modifications, and Physical Fitness and Activity Concepts

Instructional cues are key words; they are simple and brief. For example, the instructional cue, "Perform the push-up properly," is not specific. It is more meaningful to say, "Backs straight" (refer to cue number three in Figure 5.4), so students begin to understand specifically how to perform a push-up.

Physical fitness and activity concepts are knowledge and understandings concerning the what's, why's, and how's of fitness (see Chapters 11 – 14). One or two major concepts may be included in each lesson; one to two minutes total is devoted to concepts (in 10 to 15 second segments). The major purpose for including concepts in each lesson is to motivate students to want to and know how to make physical activity and fitness a regular part of their lives.

Instructional cues (and methods and organization) that apply to all of the activities are not numbered and are stated prior to the specific activities. For example the instructional cue labeled, "Modify a movement if you feel pain in your neck or low back," applies to all of the activities listed under strength and muscular endurance.

A cue or concept that corresponds with a specific activity and method is numbered appropriately. Like the activities, the instructional cues and concepts are organized from simple to complex. (Chapters 11 through 14 contain sequentially organized concepts for each health related physical fitness component; Chapter 17 presents strategies for integrating fitness concepts into the total school curriculum.)

Transitions

Transitions consist of the specific words to be used by the teacher to proceed from one activity to another. The teacher plans transitions so that as little time as possible is taken to progress from one activity to the next (see Chapter 9). Transitions between activities are separated from the activities in the lesson plan by horizontal lines.

Homework

A homework assignment, either oral, written or physical, is given to the students at the conclusion of each physical education lesson. An oral homework assignment may consist of the students asking someone at home (or the school principal!), "What happens to the heart when we are physically active?" As stated in the lesson plan, "It beats faster and gets stronger." A written assignment might consist of the students writing a paragraph about their favorite physical activity. One that involves physical activity might be for the students to dance to their favorite music for five minutes! Assigning homework is an excellent way to promote physical activity habits outside the school setting!

Summary

Although the development of physical activity and fitness habits is not the only goal of physical education, physical activity and fitness experiences and concepts are regularly included in lessons throughout the year to meet the physical education standards. Whereas a specific skill may be taught during a two-week unit and then reviewed several months later, physical activity and fitness experiences, aimed at meeting the standards, must be included in physical education lessons on a regular basis. Each of the fitness components (cardiovascular fitness, body composition, muscular strength and endurance, and flexibility) requires a minimal amount of time to be developed and maintained. The lesson plan needs to be well thought out and prepared ahead of time to ensure that students are provided with educational activities through which they can become fit and develop a love of activity. **Physical fitness activities should not be equated with recess or held as an afterthought!**

References

Corbin, C., & Lindsey, R. (2003). *Fitness for life* (6th ed.). Glenview, IL: Scott Foresman & Co.

Council on Physical Education for Children (COPEC). (1992). *Developmentally appropriate physical education practices for children: A position statement of the Council on Physical Education for Children.* Reston, VA: National Association for Sport and Physical Education (NASPE).

Graham, G., Holt/Hale, S., & Parker, M. (2007). *Children moving: A teacher's guide to developing a successful physical education program* (7th ed.). NY: McGraw-Hill.

Kirchner, G., & Fishburne, G. (2004). *Physical education for elementary school children.* (11th ed.). Dubuque, IA: William C. Brown.

NASPE. (2004). *Moving into the future: National standards for physical education: A guide to content and assessment.* (2nd ed.). Reston, VA: McGraw-Hill.

NASPE. (2004). *Physical activity for children: A statement of guidelines.* Reston, VA: NASPE.

Nichols, B. (2004). Moving and learning: *The elementary school physical education experience* (5th ed.). St Louis, MO: Times Mirror Mosby.

Pangrazi, R. (2007). *Dynamic physical education for elementary school children* (15th ed.). San Francisco, CA: Pearson Publishing.

Pate, R. (1985). Teaching physical fitness concepts in public schools. in *Implementation of health fitness exercise programs*, edited by D. Cundiff. Reston, VA: AAHPERD.

Petray, C., Leeds, M., Blazer, S., & McSwegin, P. (1989). Programming for physical fitness. *JOPERD, 60*(1), 42-46.

The National Center for Chronic Disease Prevention and Health Promotion, Centers for Disease Control and Prevention. (1997). Guidelines for school and community programs to promote lifelong physical activity among young people. *Journal of School Health, 76*(6), 202-209.

Chapter 8
Creating a Classroom Climate that Promotes Student Learning

The classroom climate has a large influence on student empowerment and learning. This chapter provides methods for creating a classroom climate that empowers students and promotes student learning. First, an approach for establishing and implementing standards for behavior that promotes fairness, equity, and respect for oneself and others is discussed. Second, the use of feedback to encourage and recognize the achievements and contributions of all students is explained. Finally, motivational strategies are presented. While each of these topics is presented separately, each area is interrelated and, when implemented together, empower students and promote student learning.

Standards for Behavior

Children choose to misbehave for many reasons. Understanding why students misbehave may help teachers prevent or curb inappropriate behavior. Teachers who make the extra effort to determine the causes of misbehavior and take appropriate action may turn the child's behavior around. Most often, a student chooses to misbehave when one or more of the following situations occur. The student:

♥ Desires attention from teachers or peers

♥ Is bored

♥ Is afraid of failing

♥ Is unable to perform an activity

♥ Does not understand the rules and consequences

♥ Thinks that the rules and consequences will not be enforced

♥ Lacks parental love, support, and attention

♥ Has a special need (ADHD, asthma, diabetes)

♥ Is angry

One of the most important determinants of a positive and empowering classroom environment is the fair and consistent implementation of rules and consequences. Most new teachers and many experienced teachers have difficulty in this area; however, establishing rules and then implementing the consequences for breaking the rules will prevent or modify most inappropriate behaviors. Consistent enforcement of rules and implementation of consequences will insure a positive classroom environment that promotes learning and empowers students to assume responsibility for themselves and one another.

Establish Rules

The teacher establishes clear rules for physical education activities; these may or may not be the same rules used in the classroom. The rules are brief, limited to no more than five, and must be enforceable. For example, the expectation "Have Fun" is not listed as a rule. While "having fun" is a desirable outcome of a quality program, it is not possible to enforce this behavior. Three rules that may be established are listed in Figure 8.1.

Figure 8.1 Physical education rules

PHYSICAL EDUCATION RULES

1. **Listen**
2. **Respect others**
3. **Hands, feet, and other body parts to yourself!**

Identify Consequences

Students must not only understand the rules, but also know the consequences that will be implemented when they choose to break the rules. Three consequences found to be effective follow (Figure 8.2).

1. **First Offense--Warning.** The student is warned; this can be done privately or in front of other classmates. Ideally, he is told specifically what the unacceptable behavior is, why it is unacceptable, and that if he chooses to continue to misbehave he will receive a time-out. While it is desirable to provide specific information concerning the misbehavior to the student, the teacher may not be able to do so. In this case, simply saying, "You have a warning," will suffice.

2. **Second Offense--Student Time-out.** When a student chooses to misbehave a second time, he receives a student time-out and is asked to sit or stand out in a previously designated area. The student is given the responsibility to rejoin the class when he is ready to follow the rules.

3. **Third Offense--Teacher Time-Out.** When a student misbehaves a third time, he receives a teacher time-out. The teacher decides when the student may rejoin the class.

Figure 8.2 Consequences for breaking the rules

PHYSICAL EDUCATION CONSEQUENCES
1. **Warning**
2. **Student time-out**
3. **Teacher time-out**

At the start of the school year or of a new physical education program, the teacher may take a lead role in identifying the rules and consequences. At some point, however, student participation in the selection of rules and consequences is encouraged. Involving students promotes the ultimate goal of having students assume responsibility for themselves and one another.

Implement Consequences

Identifying and explaining rules and consequences are the first two steps in implementing standards for behavior. The third, and most difficult step, is to enforce the rules and carry out the consequences. This requires that the teacher intervene immediately when a student chooses not to follow the rules. It is especially difficult for new teachers to give warnings and time-outs. It is much easier to use idle threats such as, "You better listen or else…" or "If you don't stop that I am going to…", than to give a time out. However, the "idle threat" approach is not effective.

When giving warnings and time-outs, the teacher explains to the student the specific behavior that is unacceptable. The message, "I like you but I don't like what you are doing," is communicated to the student.

Implementing consequences consistently involves pre-planning. Prior to each lesson, students are notified ahead of time that consequences will be implemented and time-out areas are designated (four to five carpet squares or towels spread outside the boundaries).

Establishing and maintaining standards for behavior will promote a comfortable learning environment in which students show respect for themselves and others. Children actually want the teacher to enforce rules by implementing consequences (See Figure 8.3)!

Figure 8.3 Student letter

Dear Mrs. L,

I know I haven't done much the first two days, but I had a lot of fun. I think all of us had a good time.

I hope all of you will get a good job teaching. The next time you go to teach P.E., and you see someone not doing what you want, like I didn't, be a bit harder on him. If you would have been hard on me, I would have got my act together the second day instead of the third. Thanks, I had fun.

Sincerely,
Danny P.

When a teacher responds to inappropriate behaviors in a fair and equitable manner, a positive environment is created in which students are empowered and learning is enhanced.

Promote Safety and Minimize Disruptions

The following precautions are recommended to promote a safe, comfortable learning environment. Although these are not rules and thus consequences for non-adherence are not implemented, incorporating these guidelines insures student safety and minimizes disruptions. Prior to the start of each physical education class each student takes responsibility to:

♥   Empty pockets.

♥   Tie shoes (in double bows!).

♥   Unwrap jackets from around the waist.

♥   Use the restroom.

♥   Consume water (up to one hour prior to activity is desirable).

Bathroom privileges are generally not given during activity unless it is an emergency. When students take responsibility for the above actions, class time will not be interrupted and chances of injury are minimized.

Feedback

The most effective way to let students know what they are doing right or in which area they may need to improve is to provide them with feedback about their performance or behavior. Feedback is separated into four categories: Positive Specific, Positive General, Corrective Specific and Corrective General feedback. The four types of feedback are defined and explained on the following page.

Four Types of Feedback

1. **Positive Specific Feedback.** This type of feedback states precisely what one or more students are doing well.

   ♥   "Class, you are stopping with your legs apart and knees bent."

   ♥   "Bonnie, you were looking into other people's eyes while you were running."

   ♥   "Tammie, you are keeping a space around you so that you do not bump into anyone."

2. **Positive General Feedback.** This type of feedback consists of non-specific comments that tell one or more students that they are doing well. Positive General feedback is normally directed at encouraging the students' performance or behavior.

   ♥   "Good job, Martha."

   ♥   "Nice try, Emily"

   ♥   "Great work, class."

   ♥   "That's the way to do it, Corinne"

3. **Corrective Specific Feedback.** This type of feedback states precisely what one or more students need to change.

   ♥   "Loren, try to stop with your legs apart and knees bent."

   ♥   "December, try to look into other people's eyes while you are

   ♥   running."

   ♥   "Brittany, you chose to talk while I was talking. This is a warning."

   ♥   "Katherine, this is the second time you have chosen to kick the hula hoop; that is dangerous and shows lack of respect for your friends. You have a student time-out."

   ♥   "Class, try to run inside the boundaries."

4. **Corrective General Feedback.** This type of feedback consists of non-specific comments that inform one or more students that they are performing a skill incorrectly or that their behavior is inappropriate. Corrective General feedback tends to be unclear and thus may discourage and frustrate students. Corrective General can be used effectively to give warnings and time-outs.

   ♥   "Do it better, Antonio."

   ♥   "Class, you are not doing that right."

   ♥   "Gracy, this is a warning."

   ♥   "Kim, you have a student-time out. Please rejoin the class when you are ready to follow the rules."

Each type of feedback has an important role in teacher/student communication. Positive General feedback is the easiest to use for most teachers and can be used effectively to encourage students. However, some teachers overuse Positive General and, thereby, confuse students as to what it is they are doing correctly. When Positive General feedback is overused, it loses its encouraging value and is sometimes interpreted as insincere.

In contrast to Positive General, Positive and Corrective Specific feedback tend to be more difficult for teachers to use; however, these types of feedback are most beneficial because they allow students to understand what they are doing well or what they can change. Since these types of feedback do not come naturally, it may be necessary for teachers to prepare for Positive and Corrective Specific feedback in advance of the lesson. When planning a lesson, teachers may pick one key point involved in a skill or activity on which to focus their Positive and Corrective Specific feedback. For example, when teaching students to catch a ball, it is important that the students keep their eyes on the ball. Therefore, a teacher might plan in advance to emphasize this key point through Positive and Corrective Specific feedback. Researchers have suggested that a lesson contain a ratio of four Positive Specific feedback statements to every one Corrective Specific feedback statement.

Unlike the other three types of feedback, Corrective General feedback may have negative overtones. Corrective General feedback tells the student that he or she is doing something incorrectly, but does not provide specific information as to what the student needs to change. Corrective General feedback may result in student frustration and development of negative attitudes toward physical activity. While a negative approach is to be avoided, Corrective General may be used effectively in a few instances. Two examples of effective statements employing Corrective General feedback are: "Claudia, this is a warning," and "Barry, you have a teacher time-out." In these two examples, the teacher is taking action to enforce the rules and consequences by confronting inappropriate behavior. While it would probably be more effective to state specifically what the inappropriate behavior was, at least the teacher is taking disciplinary action!

Two Types of Feedback in One Statement

Teachers may combine two or more types of feedback in the same statement. It is especially effective to precede Corrective Specific feedback with a Positive Specific or Positive General comment. Some examples follow.

- ♥ **Positive General and Corrective Specific.** "That's the way Clay; now try to bend your knees when you land."
- ♥ **Positive Specific and Corrective Specific.** "Katie, you are using the pads of your fingers as you dribble; now try to dribble the ball waist high."
- ♥ **Positive General and Positive Specific.** "Great job Jed, you are keeping your elbows in as you turn your jump rope."

Providing feedback assures students that the teacher is aware of their performance and behavior. It may also serve to motivate students to put forth maximal effort and enhance both their performance and behavior.

Motivational Strategies

The teacher plays a key role in maximizing student participation and enjoyment by planning ahead for situations that may result in student misbehavior. In addition to the effective use of feedback, a variety of instructional strategies will not only increase student motivation, but will decrease misbehavior; these strategies follow.

♥ **Include Variety.** Teach a variety of physical education activities during each lesson as well as throughout the school year. For example, including physical fitness, motor skills and a game in each lesson will minimize boredom and maximize student interest.

♥ **Avoid the Use of Physical Fitness and Activity as Punishment.** Reward students with physical activity! Students will develop a negative attitude toward fitness if they are ordered to run laps or perform push-ups for punishment. On the other hand, one teacher said to her class, "If you really give your best during Circuit Training today, I'll give you free time to walk and jog with a partner."

♥ **Provide Opportunities for Pre- Post- and Self-Measurement in Physical Activity and Fitness.** Conduct fitness measurement at the beginning, middle, and end of the school year. Provide opportunities for self-evaluation periodically and emphasize self-improvement (Chapter 16).

♥ **Solicit Student Ideas for Fitness Routines and Music.** Use student ideas to increase student interest and motivation.

♥ **Teach the Why's of Health Related Physical Fitness and Physical Activity.** Teach students simple physiological concepts that will enable them to understand the importance of physical activity and fitness to lifetime health and empower them to develop positive physical activity habits.

♥ **Keep Extrinsic Rewards to a Minimum.** Use extrinsic rewards such as ribbons, points, certificates, and badges minimally; these may result in students participating solely for the reward. The goal of a quality health related physical fitness-based physical education program is to motivate students to enjoy regular participation in physical activity—the reward is feeling good and good health!

♥ **Allow Students to Grade Themselves in Physical Education.** Give students responsibility for grading themselves. A sample Self-Grading Form is described in Chapter 16. The teacher gave her students the responsibility for assigning themselves their own grades in physical education. The grades were based upon effort, and the students themselves were truly the only ones who knew how hard they tried. The teacher reserved the right to disagree if she believed a grade given by a student was not accurate. She found that 99% of the time the students were accurate in their evaluation of themselves. More often than not, students evaluated themselves too low, rather than too high!

♥   **Teach with Enthusiasm!** If physical fitness is not **fun** for the teacher, it will not be **fun** for the students!

Summary

This chapter discusses standards for behavior, feedback, and motivational strategies. Incorporating these elements into each lesson will help to insure that physical education experiences are educational, empowering and fun for students.

References

Charles, C.M. (1992) *Building classroom discipline* (4th ed.). New York: Longman.

Gordon, A., & Brown, K.W. (1996.) *Guiding young children in a diverse society.* Boston: Allyn and Bacon.

Greci, J. (1997). Make physical education fun and exciting using music. *JOPERD, 68*(5), 12-13.

Grineski, S. (1996). *Cooperative learning in physical education.* Human Kinetics: Champaign, IL.

Gustafson, M.A., Wolfe, S.K., & King, C.L. (1991). *Great games for young people.* Human Kinetics: Champaign, IL.

Hellison, D. (2001). *Teaching responsibility through physical activity.* Champaign, IL: Human Kinetics.

Hellison, D., & Templin, T.J. (2000). *A reflective approach to teaching physical education.* Human Kinetics: Champaign, IL.

Hennessy, B.F. (1996). *Physical education sourcebook.* Human Kinetics: Champaign, IL.

Lavay, B., French, R., & Henderson, H. (2004). *Positive behavior management strategies for physical educators.* Champaign, IL: Human Kinetics.

Metzler, M. (1995). *Instructional supervision for physical education.* Human Kinetics: Champaign, IL.

Mohnsen, B. (2004). *Using technology in physical education.* Champaign, IL: Human Kinetics.

Mohnsen, B. (2000). *Teaching middle school physical education.* Champaign, IL: Human Kinetics.

Mosston, Muska and Sara Ashworth. (2000). *Teaching physical education* (5th ed.). Columbus, OH: Charles E. Merrill Publishing

Sherman, C.P. (1999). Integrating management skills into the physical education curriculum. *JOPERD, 70*(5), 25-30.

Siedentop, D. (2001). *Developing teaching skills in physical education* (5th ed.). Mountain View, CA: Mayfield.

Wolfgang, C.H. (1996). *The three faces of discipline for the elementary school teacher.* Boston: Allyn and Bacon.

Chapter 9

Optimizing Class Time to Maximize Students' Physical Activity in Physical Education

The foundation for establishing an active lifestyle is provided in physical education. Students who have fun while experiencing maximal physical activity and learning during physical education lessons are more likely to acquire the attitudes, knowledge and skills necessary to establish a physically active lifestyle. This chapter explains how to plan for effective use of class time to ensure that children spend the majority of time in the physical education lesson actively participating.

Definitions of the Time-use Categories: Activity, Instruction and Management Time

Class time in physical education can be divided into three separate time-use categories depending on what is occurring in the lesson. During a lesson the students may be active, the teacher may provide instructions, organize students and equipment, enforce standards of behavior, or the students may be waiting for a turn. The three time-use categories are Activity, Instruction and Management (AIM) time. Specific definitions of each AIM category follow.

1. **Activity time is class time during which:**
   - ♥ At least 50% of the students are performing motor activities, **and**
   - ♥ The motor activities pertain to the subject matter of physical education. Examples include the following: physical fitness activities, motor skills, exploratory movements, fundamental movements, sport skills and games.

   Both criteria must be present in the lesson for Activity time to take place.

2. **Instruction time is class time during which:**
   - ♥ Less than 50% of the students are active, **and**
   - ♥ The teacher provides information about the subject matter of physical education (such as movement and fitness concepts, physical fitness, motor skill performance, and how to play a game) with the intent that the students learn the information. The information may be provided directly by the teacher using visual aides, talking or demonstrating (teacher or student demonstration), or indirectly by soliciting information from students. Providing students with feedback about their performance can also be an example of Instruction time.

   Both criteria must be present for Instruction time to take place.

3. Management time is divided into three categories:

♥ **Organizational Management time**

♥ **Behavior Management time**

♥ **Wait time**

Organizational Management time includes the class time it takes to:

♥ distribute and collect equipment, **or**

♥ transition from one activity to another, **or**

♥ divide the students into groups or teams.

The percentage of students active is not a consideration during organizational management; more or less than 50% of the students may be active during organizational management.

Behavior Management time includes the time it takes to:

♥ interact with students about classroom rules and consequences while less than 50% of the students are active.

Explaining the rules and consequences, reinforcing them, and giving warnings and time-outs, when less than 50% of the students are active, are examples of Behavior Management time.

Wait time includes the time during which:

♥ less than 50% of the students are performing motor skills because they are standing still or in line waiting for a turn during a game or other activity, and no subject matter is being taught. Kickball, softball and relays are three examples of activities comprised entirely of Wait time.

Only one of the above criteria must be present for Management time to take place.

Optimizing AIM

An effective teacher optimizes the use of class time by providing maximal time for all students to participate in physical activity, providing clear and concise instruction, teaching and enforcing standards for behavior and providing efficient transitions. The following are instructional strategies aimed at using class time effectively and efficiently.

Instructional Strategies for Optimizing Activity Time

Physical Education is the only subject in the curriculum that involves movement. The majority of the time in each lesson is to be devoted to Activity time. Ideally, Activity time should comprise at least 70% of class time in each lesson. Some strategies optimizing Activity time follow.

✳ 1.   Provide Time for Exploration. Allow students free time to explore when they first get a piece of equipment. This strategy promotes Activity time when compared to the approach of having students get a piece of equipment, place it at their feet and listen to instructions before having the chance to use it.

✳ 2.   Modify Activity to Include Everyone. Provide alternative activities for students who cannot participate in the regular activity. For example, encourage students with low fitness levels to march in place when they get tired during cardiovascular fitness activities.

3.   Talk While Students are Active. When possible, avoid stopping an activity to provide instruction or manage students. Instead, talk to students while they are involved in activity. For example, a teacher may say: "Class, that's the way to make eye contact while you're running" while all the students are running inside the boundaries.

4.   Provide Ample Equipment. Provide every child with his own piece of equipment, just as each child has his own reading and math books.

5.   Involve 100 Percent of Students. Incorporate games and activities that promote maximal activity for all students such as High Five Tag or Back to Back (Chapter 15). Modify elimination games such as traditional Freeze Tag, in which students are out when they are tagged. If modification is not possible, eliminate inactive and elimination games in favor of activities in which all students actively participate.

6.   Circulate Among Students. Move throughout the students constantly during the physical education activities so that there is no "front" of the class. When the teacher gets closer to students they are more likely to stay active and on task.

7.   Use Appropriate Feedback. Students become motivated to actively participate when they are given appropriate feedback (see Chapter 8).

8.   Use Students' Names. Use each student's name as frequently as possible to motivate and provide feedback.

9. **Use Music.** Incorporate music into the physical education lesson, especially the students' favorite music.

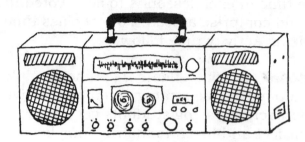

Instructional Strategies for Optimizing Instruction Time

Quality physical education instruction provides students with the knowledge they need to perform skills and exercises correctly as well as to develop an active lifestyle. Most teachers talk too much; effective teachers identify information essential for student learning and present it in the most efficient manner. Ideally, Instruction time is less than 20% of each lesson. Instructional strategies for optimizing Instruction time follow.

1. **Provide Brief Instructions.** Keep talking to a minimum. Students cannot become fit or learn a skill while listening to instructions. Limit talking to less than 30 seconds at any one time whenever possible.

2. **Model Activities.** Participate with the students whenever possible. Most children learn more from what they see than from what they are told. An adult cannot sit under a tree and ask children to "keep going" and "work up a sweat"--it will not work!

3. **Use Students' Names.** Using students' names when providing both feedback and student demonstrations makes the instruction more personal and thus may increase its meaning to the students.

4. **Incorporate Student and Teacher Demonstrations.** Use student and teacher demonstrations while orally instructing students to give students a visual picture of what you expect; these demonstrations may even decrease the need for certain verbal instructions. Moreover, if students know the teacher is looking for people to demonstrate, they will perform even better. Students may also be more comfortable attempting an activity that their peer has demonstrated.

✸5. **Use Specific Feedback.** Provide individual students and the class as a whole with Positive and Corrective Specific feedback during activity to reinforce the desired skill or behavior. For example, "Clay, you have stopped with your legs apart, now try to bend your knees." Providing specific feedback tells a student precisely what he is doing well or needs to improve, whereas general statements such as "Good job" are vague. Chapter 8 includes an explanation of the different types of feedback.

6. **Minimize the Use of Inappropriate and Overused Words and Phrases.** Many times teachers repeat a filler word (a word used during a pause in speech) such as "Okay" or "Um." The phrase "You guys" is gender biased. Questions such as "Are there any questions?" and "Do You Understand?" may elicit conflicting student responses such as "yes," "no," and "I don't know," and usually result in wasted time. Inappropriate and overused words and phrases can also distract students from the content of the instructions being provided. Ultimately, minimizing inappropriate and overused words and phrases may optimize Instruction time.

7. **Use Visual Aides.** Use signs, posters and instructional aides to help teach and reinforce major concepts. For example, use bone and muscle flash cards that ask a question on one side and have the answer on the other.

| What happens to our heart when we are active? | It beats faster and it gets stronger!! |

8. **Use Cue Words to Teach One Key Point at a Time.** Break complex activities into many simple movements and use cue words. For example, When teaching children how to throw, students first learn to step with the leg opposite the throwing arm. The cue word is "step." Teach one part of a skill, let the students participate, and then teach the next part. Continue introducing one key point at a time and allowing students to practice.

9. **Teach Activities in Progression.** Teach the easiest skill first and build gradually. For example, students learning to jump rope start by jumping over a rope on the floor, and progress to turning the rope with both handles in one hand before actually try to jump the rope. Similarly, a bent knee push-up is taught before a regular push-up. Fitness routines start at a low enough level so each child can progress at her own rate without being compared to others. When students participate in activities that progress from easy to more difficult, they are more likely to develop feelings of competence that lead to confidence.

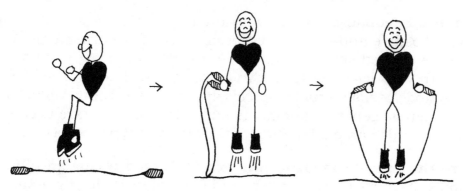

10. **Face the Sun When Giving Instructions.** Face the sun when giving important instructions. It is difficult for students to pay attention to instructions when they are looking into the sun.

Instructional Strategies for Optimizing Management Time

Management time comprises the lowest percentage of time in the physical education lesson; however, it may ultimately determine the success of a lesson. Ideally, Management time constitutes less than 10% of each lesson. Strategies for optimizing each of the three categories of Management time follow.

1.   Behavior Management time

♥   *Collaborate With Students When Establishing Rules and Consequences.* Teacher and student collaboration when selecting rules and consequences encourages compliance and reinforces the importance of the rules.

♥   *Limit Rules and Consequences.* Limit the rules and consequences to no more than four. More than four rules and consequences are difficult to remember as well as to enforce.

♥   *Explain Rules and Consequences.* At the beginning of the school year, review the rules and the consequences for breaking the rules at the beginning of each class.

✳ ♥   *Check for Comprehension.* Ask each student to explain the rules and consequences to a partner. Then ask one or two students to explain them to the class.

♥   *Post Rules and Consequences.* Post rules and consequences in a visible location at a readable distance (20 to 30 feet) from the physical education class as a constant reminder of the agreement made between student and teacher. A bulletin board may be used in an indoor activity area or a poster may be made for outdoor activities.

♥   *Enforce Rules and Consequences Consistently from the Beginning.* Implement the consequences at the first sign of misbehavior; this develops student respect for the rules. Treat all children in a fair, equitable way; avoid favoring one student over another. If the teacher ignores some misbehaviors and responds to others, students may become confused and lose respect for the importance of the rules.

♥   *Designate at Least Two Time-out Areas Ahead of Time.* Clearly designate time-out areas prior to the start of activity (carpet squares or towels may be used). When students know immediately where to go when a time-out is given, less time is wasted on management. Establish separate "time-out areas" so students in time-out do not stand or sit together.

♥ *Ask students in Time-out to Turn Their Backs to the Activity.* Students may try to make faces at the rest of the class behind your back! Accordingly, they turn their backs to the activity and are not allowed to talk to classmates or touch equipment.

♥ *Minimize Time in Time-outs.* Do not keep students out of activity for a long period of time. It Is easy to get distracted and to forget about students after putting them in time-out! Ideally, students rejoin the class in less than one minute (except in extreme cases).

♥ *Use Students' Names.* Engage and motivate students by using their names to acknowledge their participation. Try to use student's names equitably.

♥ *Provide Appropriate Feedback.* Provide positive feedback to reinforce the desired skill or behavior. Provide corrective specific feedback to maximize student learning and success.

♥ *Utilize Student Demonstrations.* Give students the attention they desire in a positive way.

♥ *Circulate Among the Students (Teacher Movement).* Move around the area and among the students during the activities. Students' behavior tends to improve when the teacher gets closer!

2. Organizational Management time

♥ *Establish Boundaries.* Designate clear and definitive boundaries for the physical education class using cones or lines on the blacktop.

✳ ♥   *Set Up Equipment Ahead of Time.* Set up equipment before class begins. This allows the teacher to transition quickly between activities.

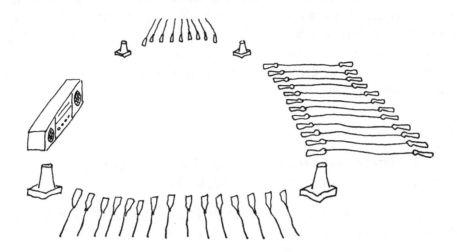

♥   *Distribute and Collect Equipment Using Several Access Points.* Place equipment at various locations outside the boundaries. This provides for quick access to and collection of equipment.

♥   *Use a Consistent Stopping Signal That is Easily Heard.* Use one stopping signal, such as a whistle or tambourine, to signal students when to stop. Avoid using the stopping signal to also signal starting as students may become confused.

♥   *Have Students Place Equipment on the Ground When Talking.* Instruct students to place their equipment on the ground at their feet when you are talking. Students are more likely to listen if equipment is out of their hands.

♥   *Say "When" and "How" Before "What."* When giving directions, tell the students <u>when</u> to move, <u>how</u> to move, and then <u>what</u> to do. For example: "When I say "heart," how quickly can you stand with a partner?"

♥   *Transition Efficiently.* Proceed from one activity to the next activity within 10 to 30 seconds. For example, if you are finished instructing with jump ropes and are proceeding on to use the parachute, direct the students to run quickly and place their jump ropes outside of the classroom boundaries (no neat piles!), and run back inside the boundaries to spread out the parachute. Use key words related to the lesson concept; for example, "When I say 'heart,' how quickly can you put your ropes outside the cones and come spread out the parachute?" "HEART!"

♥   *Select Groups Using Efficient Non-Discriminatory Methods.* Three team selection methods that may embarrass or discriminate are: 1) using team captains to select teams, 2) dividing based upon gender (boys and girls) and 3) grouping based upon eye or hair color or any other physical characteristic that would result in cultural bias. The use of numbering off students is also discouraged; it is time consuming and can become disruptive when students reposition themselves to get the same number as their friend (Chapter 15).

3.   Wait time

✱♥   *Modify Activities to Include Everyone.* Provide alternatives to or omit elimination games to decrease student Wait time.

♥   *Provide Ample Equipment.* Provide at least one piece of equipment per student to avoid Wait time and optimize Activity time.

♥   *Use Groups of no More Than Two.* Use groups of no more than two to minimize turn taking. Using groups of two ensures that at least 50% of the students are active and thus prevents Wait time from occurring. Using groups of two instead of groups of three changes Wait time to Activity time.

Summary

A primary goal of quality physical education programs is to provide enjoyable physical education experiences in which all students can be active and successful. Physical education teachers can use the instructional strategies presented in this chapter to plan physical education lessons that provide maximal opportunity for all students to actively participate. These strategies may also be used to limit instruction time to essential information necessary for students' success and learning as well as to optimize Management time by consistently enforcing rules and consequences and efficiently organizing students and equipment.

References

Council on Physical Education for Children (COPEC). (1992). *Developmentally appropriate physical education practices for children: A position statement of the Council on Physical Education for Children.* Reston, VA: National Association for Sport and Physical Education.

NASPE. (1994). *Appropriate instructional practice for elementary school physical education.* Reston VA: AAHPERD.

NASPE. (2005). *Moving into the future: National standards for physical education: A guide to content and assessment.* St. Louis, MO: Mosby.

NASPE. (2004). *Physical activity for children: A statement of guidelines.* (2nd ed.). Reston, VA: NASPE Publications.

Petray, C., Williams, E., Lavay, B. & Hakim-Butt, K. (2002). Ongoing Systematic Self-Assessment of Pre-service Physical Education Teachers' Teaching Behaviors. *JOPERD, 73*(7), 47-55.

Chapter 10

Self-Evaluating and Reflecting on the Teaching Process

The process of observing and reflecting about one's own teaching can be one of the most powerful methods of learning about teaching. Chapter 9 presents instructional strategies for using class time effectively, including strategies for maximizing Activity time, optimizing Instruction time, and minimizing Management time. This chapter provides techniques for self-evaluating and reflecting on certain measurable instructional strategies that affect how time is used in the physical education lesson.

To conduct the self-evaluation and reflection described in this chapter, the teacher's lesson is recorded for viewing using any available technology. The process of watching a lesson and recording certain instructional strategies is referred to as coding. The teacher can use the instruments presented in the chapter to code her lesson for the following instructional strategies and AIM time (Chapters 8 and 9).

♥   Teacher Movement, Teacher Demonstrations, Student Demonstrations
♥   Names
♥   Inappropriate and Overused Words and Phrases
♥   Feedback

Once several lessons are coded, the data can be graphed to create a visual representation of progress. Sample graphs that chart progress in four of these areas over an eight-week period are provided

Teacher Movement, Teacher Demonstrations, and Student Demonstrations

Three instructional strategies that can be coded at the same time are teacher movement and teacher and student demonstrations. Moving throughout the students so that there is no "front" of the classroom may maximize Activity time and minimize Management time because children are more likely to be active and are less likely to misbehave when the teacher moves closer to them. Incorporating teacher and student demonstrations may decrease the need for specific spoken directions and therefore may optimize Instruction time. Additionally, the use of student demonstrations may minimize Management time because it gives students the attention they desire in a positive way.

Figure 10.1 shows an instrument that may be used to code teacher movement and teacher and student demonstrations. This instrument includes a cross sectional that represents the classroom divided into four quadrants. A "T" is recorded on the cross sectional each time the teacher moves to a different location and stops; the initial starting point is bolded. Arrows from one "T" to another denote the direction of the teacher's movement. Similarly, when the teacher provides a demonstration (TD) or initiates a student demonstration (SD), the corresponding abbreviation is placed in the appropriate quadrant. After coding for these three strategies, the teacher tallies the number of teacher and student demonstrations and places each total in the appropriate "Total" space. The sample in Figure 10.1 shows that the teacher moved through all four quadrants of the class. It also shows that four teacher demonstrations (TD) and two student demonstrations (SD) were used. Once the teacher codes for this information, he reflects on the patterns of his movement and his use of both teacher and student demonstrations.

Figure 10.1   Coding of and reflection on teacher movement, teacher demonstrations and student demonstrations

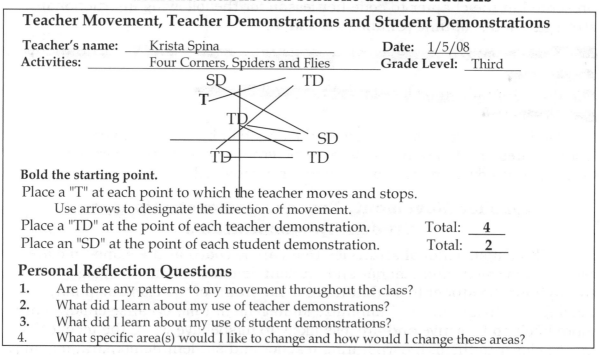

Teacher Movement, Teacher Demonstrations and Student Demonstrations

Teacher's name: Krista Spina   Date: 1/5/08
Activities: Four Corners, Spiders and Flies   Grade Level: Third

Bold the starting point.
Place a "T" at each point to which the teacher moves and stops.
    Use arrows to designate the direction of movement.
Place a "TD" at the point of each teacher demonstration.   Total: __4__
Place an "SD" at the point of each student demonstration.   Total: __2__

Personal Reflection Questions
1.   Are there any patterns to my movement throughout the class?
2.   What did I learn about my use of teacher demonstrations?
3.   What did I learn about my use of student demonstrations?
4.   What specific area(s) would I like to change and how would I change these areas?

After coding and reflecting on the teacher movement and teacher and student demonstrations in a lesson, the teacher sets goals for future lessons and continues to monitor his progress.

Student Names

Another instructional strategy that can be coded is the teacher's use of students' names; the use of names may affect all three time-use categories. For example, Activity time may be maximized because students become motivated to participate when their name is used. Instruction time may be optimized when a teacher uses students' names when providing both feedback and student demonstrations. Management time may be minimized because students are less likely to choose to misbehave if their name is used in a positive way.

Figure 10.2 shows an instrument that may be used to code the teacher's use of students' names during a lesson. First, the teacher either lists the names of all the students in the class or obtains a class roster. The teacher then totals the number of times each student's name is stated. The sample in Figure 10.2 shows that the name Luis is followed by the number 3. This means that during the lesson, the teacher stated Luis' name three times.

In section I, the teacher identifies each student name that was not stated. The sample shows that the following names were not used: Katie, Holly, Alicia, Rocky, Jennifer, Bjorn, Bonnie, Clay, Ryan, Bill, Tammie, Albert, Sierra, Ernesto, Tamra, Jed, Jeanette, Frances, Patricia, Kimberly, Corinne, Henry, Jessica, Erika and Kit.

In section II, the teacher enters the total number of students in the class, records the number of different student's names in the class stated and then calculates the percentage of total students' names in the class stated. The sample shows that 5 out of 30 (17%) of the student's names were stated in that lesson.

In section III, the teacher enters the total number of females and the total number of males in the class. He then records the number of different female and different male names stated and calculates the percentages for each gender. The sample shows that two out of 18 female's names (11%) and that three out of 12 male's names (25%) were stated in the lesson. Once the teacher calculates the percentage of total names percentage of male and females names stated, he reflects on whether or not he is using names equitably.

Figure 10.2 Coding of and reflecting on the use of student names

---

Student Names

Teacher's name: _____ Stacey Cargnalutti _____ Date: _2/14/08_
Activities: _____ Circuit Training, Alligators and Gorillas _____ Grade Level: _Third_

List the names of all students in the class or obtain a class list. Total the number of times you say each student's name.

Luis **3**	Su **1**	Katie	Holly	Alicia	Rocky
Bjorn	Bonnie	Clay	Ryan	Bill	Jennifer
Maria **2**	Tammie	Albert	Sierra	Ernesto	Tamra
Jed	Jeanette	Frances	Trevor **1**	Patricia	Kimberly
Corinne	Carlos **2**	Henry	Jessica	Erika	Kit

I. **List student names in the class not stated.**

Katie	Holly	Alicia	Rocky	Jennifer
Bjorn	Bonnie	Clay	Ryan	Bill
Tammie	Albert	Sierra	Ernesto	Tamra
Jed	Jeanette	Frances	Patricia	Kimberly
Corinne	Henry	Jessica	Erika	Kit

II. **Percent of different names in the class stated:** **17%**
  A. Total number of students in the class: 30
  B. Number of different student names in the class stated: 5

III. **Percent of different student names by gender**
  A. Total number of females in the class: 18
  B. Total number of males in the class: 12
  C. Number of different female names in the class stated: 2
  D. Number of different male names in the class stated: 3
  E. **Percent of females' names in the class stated:** **11%**
  F. **Percent of males' names in the class stated:** **25 %**

IV. **Personal Reflection Questions**
  A. Is there a trend or pattern to my use of student names?
  B. Which student's names do I state the least? The most?
  C. Do I favor one gender? If so, which one?
  D. What changes would I like to make concerning my use of names?

After coding and reflecting on her use of student names in a lesson, the teacher sets goals for future lessons and continues to monitor her progress. Figure 10.3 shows a graph of one teacher's results after coding four lessons over an eight-week period.

Figure 10.2 Coding of and reflecting on the use of student names

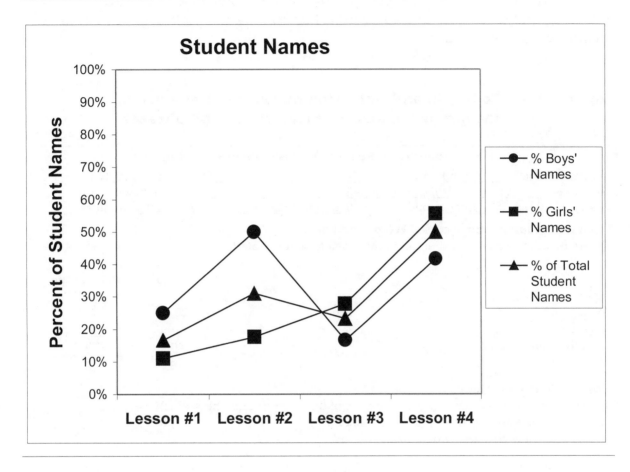

The graph in Figure 10.3 shows that the teacher progressed from using 17% of students' names on day one to 50% on day four. In the area of gender, the teacher progressed from using 25% of the males' and 11% of the females' names on day one to 42% and 56%, respectively, on day four. Graphing this data allows the teacher to monitor her progress in the area of use of student names and to set goals for future lessons. Most importantly, further reflection naturally follows from this visual representation.

Inappropriate and Overused Words and Phrases

The teacher can also code her use of inappropriate and overused words and phrases. Minimizing the use of such words and phrases may positively affect Instruction time because instructions will be more succinct.

Figure 10.4 shows an instrument for coding inappropriate and overused words and phrases stated during the lesson. Coding these words and phrases is similar to coding use of names during a lesson; the teacher totals the number of times she uses each word or phrase. Additionally, a teacher

phrases. Coding one's use of these words and phrases during a lesson will increase the teacher's awareness of her speech patterns and aid her in reflecting on whether or not she would like to make any changes in her use of certain words or phrases.

Figure 10.4   Coding of and reflection on the teacher's use of inappropriate and overused words and phrases

---

Inappropriate and Overused Words and Phrases

Teacher's name: _____ Sandy Blazer _____ Date: _3/19/08_

Activities: ____ Astronaut drills, hula hoops _____ Grade Level: _Third_

Lesson Length: _1889_ total seconds / _30 minutes, 29 seconds_ / _30.5_ minutes

Total Inappropriate and overused Words and Phrases: _____ 113 _____

Please place tally marks next to the phrase each time it is stated.

	Total	Per minute
"Okay"	<u>28</u>	<u>.9</u>
"You guys"	<u>20</u>	<u>.7</u>
"Good job"	<u>40</u>	<u>1.3</u>
"Are there any questions?"	<u>10</u>	<u>.3</u>
"Excellent"	<u>15</u>	<u>.5</u>

Personal Reflection Questions
1. Are there any trends or patterns to my use of these words and phrases?
2. Do I overuse any words or phrases not listed?
3. Are there any changes I would like to make?

After coding his lesson for inappropriate and overused words and phrases and reflecting on this information, the teacher sets goals for future lessons and continues to monitor his progress. Figure 10.5 depicts one teacher's results after coding four lessons over an eight-week period. The frequency per minute of each inappropriate word and phrase is graphed.

The graph shows that the teacher progressed from using "you guys" .7 times per minute, "okay" .9 times per minute, "good job" 1.3 times per minute, "are there any questions?" .3 times per minute, and "excellent" .5 times per minute on day one to .5, .8, .7, .2, and .1 respectively, on day four. Graphing this data allows the teacher to monitor his progress in the area of inappropriate and overused words and phrases and to set goals for future lessons. Most importantly, further reflection naturally follows from this visual representation.

Figure 10.5   Graph of frequency of inappropriate and overused words and phrases

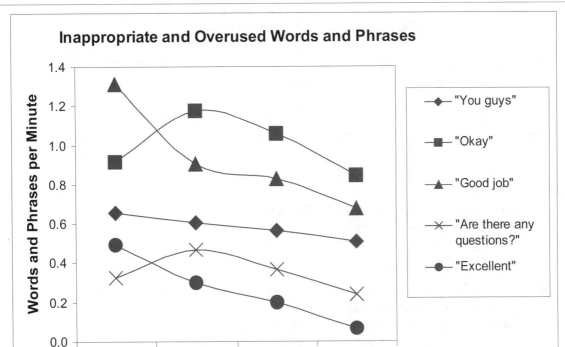

Feedback

The teacher's feedback (Chapter 8) to the students can also be coded; the use of appropriate feedback may affect all three AIM categories. For example, Activity time may be affected because students become motivated to participate when they are given appropriate feedback. Instruction time may be affected because appropriate feedback provides the students with information that can reinforce the desired skill performance. Management time may be affected because students are less likely to choose to misbehave if they are receiving appropriate feedback about their performance or behavior.

Figure 10.6 depicts an instrument on which the teacher has recorded his feedback and has labeled it as either Positive Specific (PS), Positive General (PG), Corrective Specific (CS) or Corrective General (CG). If a certain feedback is repeated more than once, it is listed once and the number of times it is used is placed in parentheses. For example, the comment, 'Good job" was stated forty times. After coding the feedback the totals for each feedback category are recorded. The sample shows that two examples of Positive Specific, 55 examples of Positive General, five examples of Corrective Specific, and twelve examples of Corrective General feedback were used. Once the totals are determined, the teacher reflects how to balance his use of feedback.

Figure 10.6   Coding of and reflection on feedback

Positive Specific (PS), Positive General (PG), Corrective Specific (CS), and Corrective General (CG) Feedback.

Teacher's name: June Duarte   Date: 4/23/08

Activities: Squad leader , parachute, basketball skills   Grade Level: Third

Lesson Length :   1893 total seconds / 30 minutes, 33 seconds   /   30.5 minutes

Please record each feedback statement, label it, and total each category.

PS 2   .07   PG 55   1.8   CS 5   .16   CG 12   .4
  total   per minute   total   per minute   total   per minute   total   per minute

Type

CS (3) 1. "You guys are outside the cones, try to come inside the boundaries, okay?"
PG (20) 2. "Good job"
PS   3. "That's the way to stay inside the boundaries."
PG (7) 4. "Good Job … (student's name)"
PG (8) 5. "You guys did a good job on that."
CG (3) 6. "You have a warning"
PG (9) 7. "Way to go, class"
CS   8. "You guys are going to bump into each other, try to make eye contact, okay?"
CG (7) 9. "Come on, class, do it right, okay?"
PS   10. "That's the way to make eye contact with each other."
CS   11. "You were talking when I was talking, you were not listening"
CG (2) 12. "You have a student time-out, okay"
PG (9) 13. "Super"
PG (2) 14. "Perfect"

Personal Reflection Questions

A. Is there a trend or pattern to my use of feedback?
B. Which type of feedback do I state the least? The most?
C. What changes would I like to make concerning my use of feedback?

After coding feedback and reflecting on his use of feedback in a lesson, the teacher sets goals for future lessons and continues to monitor his progress. Figure 10.7 depicts one teacher's results after coding four lessons over an eight-week period; each type of feedback is graphed as frequency of use per minute.

Figure 10.7   Graph of frequency of individual feedback

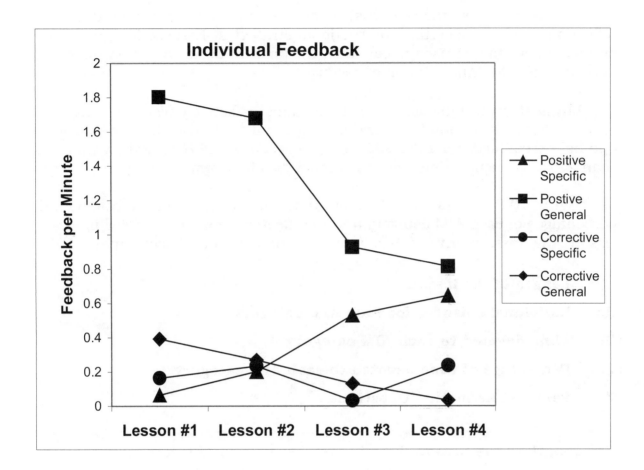

The graph in Figure 10.7 shows that the teacher progressed from using positive specific .07 times per minute, positive general 1.8 times per minute, corrective specific .16 times per minute, and corrective general .40 times per minute, on day one to .5, .6, .3, and .03 respectively, on day four. Graphing this data allows the teacher to monitor his progress in the area of use of feedback and to set goals for future lessons. Most importantly, further reflection naturally follows from this visual representation.

Activity, Instruction, and Management (AIM) Time

Teachers can use the previously explained instruments to record and reflect on their use of certain instructional strategies. This section presents an instrument that is used to calculate the amount of Activity, Instruction and Management (AIM) time in a lesson.

Physical education class time is used most effectively by optimizing Activity time, Instruction time, and Management time (see Chapter 9). The optimal percentages for each AIM category are: at least 70% Activity time, less than 20% Instruction time and less than 10% Management time.

Figure 10.8 depicts an instrument that may be used both to calculate the percentages of each AIM category and to reflect on how time is used in a lesson. This instrument consists of five sections organized sequentially (I-V):

I.   **Length of the lesson**

II. **Individual episodes for each AIM category**

III. **Time devoted to each AIM category**

IV. **Percentage of time devoted to each AIM category**

V.   **Personal Reflection Questions.**

I.   **Length of the Lesson.** First the teacher times and records the length of the lesson in minutes and seconds. The minutes and seconds are then converted to total seconds for use in subsequent calculations. In the following sample, the lesson length is 30 minutes and 27 seconds, recorded as 1827 seconds in section I of the AIM instrument.

II. **Individual Episodes for Each AIM Category.** In section "II," the teacher uses a stopwatch to time each specific episode of Activity, Instruction and Management time and records it to the nearest second in the appropriate category. For example, if the teacher begins the lesson with a 195-second discussion about the rules and consequences, the number 195 is recorded as the first Management time episode. If the teacher then proceeds with a 27-second explanation related to the subject matter, the number 27 is recorded as the first Instruction time episode. If the students are then involved in practicing a skill activity for 35 seconds, the number 35 is recorded as the first Activity time episode. The teacher continues to time each episode as it occurs in the lesson and record it in the appropriate AIM category. When the timing and recording of the episodes is completed, the teacher labels (a, b, c, d, e) each episode greater than 30 seconds for both Instruction and Management time. In the sample, three episodes of Instruction time and four episodes of Management time are longer than 30 seconds and are thus labeled. Each labeled episode is addressed specifically under section V.

III. **Class Time Devoted to Each Aim Category.** In this section, the teacher adds the episodes in each specific category and records the total seconds in the appropriate AIM category. In the sample there are thirteen episodes of Activity time totaling 456 seconds; the number 456 is recorded under section III A--Activity time. Similarly, the total seconds for Instruction and Management time, 639 and 730 respectively, are recorded under III B and C.

IV. **Percentage of Class Time Devoted to Each Aim Category.** In section IV, the percentage of class time devoted to each AIM category is calculated. The total time in seconds devoted to each category, found in section III, is individually divided by the length of the lesson in total seconds (from section I). In the sample, the percentage of Activity time is determined by dividing the total time in seconds devoted to Activity time (456) by the length of the lesson in total seconds (1827). Similarly, 639 (total seconds of Instruction time) and 730 (total seconds of Management time) are both divided by 1827 to determine the percent of class time devoted to Instruction and Management time.

V. **Personal Reflection Questions.** Once the percentages of Activity, Instruction and Management time are calculated, they may be compared to the target AIM percentages. After making this comparison, the teacher reflects on whether more or less time needs to be devoted to each time-use category. If changes in the AIM percentages are desired, the teacher identifies specific instructional strategies that can be implemented into future lessons to achieve the desired changes. Additionally, the teacher refers to section II to determine whether or not her Instruction and Management time episodes of greater than 30 seconds can be shortened. Personal reflection contains an acknowledgment of both positive teaching strategies and areas for improvement.

Figure 10.8   Coding of and reflection on activity, instruction, and management time (AIM)

Activity, Instruction, and Management (AIM) Time Self-Evaluation

Student Teacher's name: <u>Jodi Parker</u>   Date: <u>5/14/2008</u>   Teaching Day: <u>1</u>
Activities: <u>Locomotor Movements, Jump Rope Skills</u>   Grade Level: <u>3</u>

I.   **Length of the Lesson**
    A.   **In total seconds**   <u>1827</u> total seconds
    B.   **In minutes and seconds**   <u>30 minutes 27 seconds</u>
    C.   **To the nearest tenth of a minute**   <u>30.45 equals 30.5 minutes</u>

II. **Individual Episodes for Each AIM Category.** Record the time of each episode to the nearest second devoted to each AIM category. Bold and label **(a,b,c,d,e)** each episode greater than 30 seconds for both Instruction and Management time. Address each of these episodes greater than 30 seconds (Instruction and Management time only) specifically in section V below.

A.	**Activity Time**	35	26	48	26	49	33	40
		25	30	50	37	35	22	
B.	**Instruction Time**	27	28	29	25	27	28	144-a
		147-b	26	57-c	26	29	20	26
C.	**Management Time**	195-d	26	25	47-e	26	71-f	28
		22	15	19	27	29	18	182-g

III. **Class Time Devoted to Each AIM Category.** Record the total time in seconds devoted to each AIM category.

    A. **Activity Time**   <u>456</u>   seconds
    B. **Instruction Time**   <u>639</u>   seconds
    C. **Management Time**   <u>730</u>   seconds
    D. **TOTAL SECONDS**   <u>1825</u>   seconds   (needs to be within 10 seconds of I.)

IV. **Percent of Class Time Devoted to Each AIM Category.** Calculate the percent of class time devoted to each category (divide the total seconds for each category by the length of the lesson in total seconds).

    A. **Activity Time**   <u>25</u>   %   (70% or more is target)
    B. **Instruction Time**   <u>35</u>   %   (20% or less is target)
    C. **Management Time**   <u>40</u>   %   (10% or less is target)
    D. **TOTAL PERCENT**   <u>100</u>   %   (needs to be within 5% of 100%.)

V.   **Personal Reflection.** Please reflect on one thing you did well in each AIM category. Reflect on the changes you would make in your lesson to decrease each Instruction and Management time episode greater than 30 seconds (II. B and C).

    A.   **To Maximize Activity Time:** Circulated among the students, had one piece of equipment for each student
    B.   **To Optimize Instruction Time:** Used visual aids for locomotor movements, **a+b)** shorten explanation of Four Corners, **c)** Don't ask "Are there any questions?"
    C.   **To Minimize Management Time:** Used whistle as a stopping signal, **d)** shorten explanation of rules and consequences, **e)** give warnings sooner, **f)** shorten transition to Four Corners, **g)** decrease time for closure and homework

After coding her lesson for Activity, Instruction and Management time, the teacher sets goals for future lessons and continues to monitor his progress. Figure 10.9 depicts one teacher's results after coding four lessons over an eight-week period.

Figure 10.9   Graph of activity, instruction, and management time (AIM)

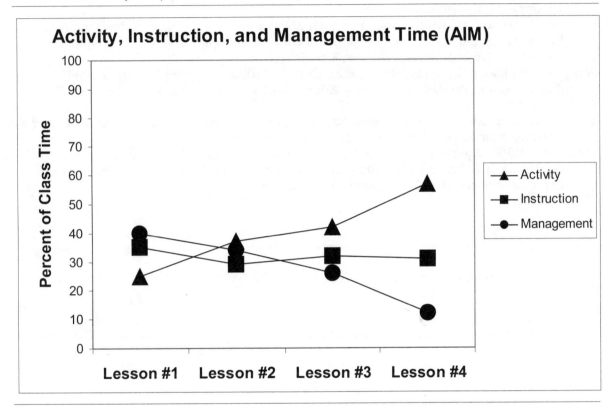

The graph in Figure 10.9 shows that the teacher progressed from 25% Activity time, 35% Instruction time, and 40% Management time on day one, to 57%, 31%, and 12% respectively, on day four. Graphing AIM data allows the teacher to monitor his progress and to set goals for future lessons. Most importantly, further reflection naturally follows from this visual representation.

Summary

Self-evaluating and reflecting on one's teaching is an ongoing process. The self-evaluation and reflection process presented in this chapter allows the teacher to objectively evaluate and reflect on his teaching. This process is aimed at improving student learning and enriching the teaching environment. The ultimate goal is to provide enjoyable physical education lessons in which students are active for a large percentage of class time, experience success and in which they develop confidence about their ability to participate in physical activity.

References

Anderson, W.G. (1980). *Analysis of teaching physical education.* St. Louis, MO: Mosby.

Cusimano, B., Darst, P., & van der Mars, H. (1993, October). Improving your teaching through self-evaluation. *Strategies,* 26-29.

Hastad, D., & Lacy, A. (2003). *Measurement and evaluation in contemporary physical education* (3rd ed.). Scottsdale, AZ: Gorsuch Scarisbrick.

Hellison, D., & Timplin, T. (1991). *A reflective approach to teaching physical education.* Champaign, IL: Human Kinetics.

Housner, L. (1996). Innovation and change in physical education. In S. Silverman & C. Ennis (Eds.), *Student learning in physical education: Applying research to enhance instruction.* Champaign, IL: Human Kinetics.

Petray, C., Williams, E., Lavay, B. & Hakim-Butt, K. (2002). Ongoing Systematic Self-Assessment of Pre-service Physical Education Teachers' Teaching Behaviors. *JOPERD, 73*(7), 47-55.

Silverman, S., & Ennis, C. (1996). *Student learning in physical education: Applying research to enhance instruction.* Champaign, IL: Human Kinetics.

Stroot, S. (1996). Organizational socialization: Factors impacting beginning teachers. In S. Silverman & C. Ennis (Eds.), *Student learning in physical education: Applying research to enhance instruction.* Champaign, IL: Human Kinetics.

PART FOUR

Physical Activity and Fitness Concepts and Activities

Chapters 11-14 present concepts and activities for each health-related physical fitness component; concepts related to physical activity are integrated into each of the chapters. These activities are designed to be fun, promote student success and provide children with the knowledge, activities, and skills needed to establish and maintain a physically active lifestyle.

Chapter 11: "Cardiovascular Fitness"
Chapter 12: "Body Composition"
Chapter 13: "Muscular Strength and Endurance"
Chapter 14: "Flexibility"

Chapter 15, "Games Without Lines: Everybody Active!" includes active games that are fun and insure maximal student participation. Efficient team selection methods that avoid student humiliation and discrimination are presented

Chapter 16, "Assessment of Physical Fitness and Physical Activity," focuses on fitness and activity assessment as an educational experience during which the process of learning about how to become fit and active is more important than the product of fitness scores.

Chapter 11
Cardiovascular Fitness

A quality health related physical fitness-based physical education program provides positive experiences through which children can assess, achieve and maintain cardiovascular fitness throughout the year. Cardiovascular fitness activities are to be FUN and are to promote each child's perception of competence and confidence about his ability to assess, achieve and maintain fitness in this area. The contents of this chapter are organized as follows:

♥ Cardiovascular Fitness Concepts
♥ Cardiovascular Fitness Activities

Significantly more concepts and activities are included in this chapter, than in Chapters 12 – 14, because of the influence of cardiovascular fitness on one's risk for heart disease and ability to carry out a physically active lifestyle.

CARDIOVASCULAR FITNESS CONCEPTS

The concepts in this chapter apply to cardiovascular fitness and are organized into "what's," "why's," and "how's." Chapter 3 provides in-depth information on cardiovascular fitness; please review this chapter prior to reading through the concepts. Teaching concepts is as important as the cardiovascular fitness activities themselves; with these understandings, students may be motivated to participate in cardiovascular fitness activity outside the school setting. It is advisable to read through all the concepts before selecting one or two for each lesson. The concepts are divided into four sections:

♥ The "What's, Why's, and How's" of Cardiovascular Fitness
♥ The "What's, Why's, and How's" of the Heart
♥ The "What's, Why's, and How's" of the Lungs
♥ The "What's, Why's, and How's" of the Blood Vessels

The "What's" of Cardiovascular Fitness

1. *What is cardiovascular fitness?* Cardiovascular fitness is the fitness of the heart, lungs, and blood vessels. "Cardio" means heart and "vascular" means blood vessels. Cardiovascular fitness is the ability of the circulatory and respiratory systems to supply oxygen during continuous physical activity. Cardiovascular fitness is sometimes referred to as aerobic ("with air") or cardiorespiratory ("heart" and "lung") fitness.

2. ***What is a healthy level of cardiovascular fitness?*** A healthy level of cardiovascular fitness allows the heart, lungs, and blood vessels to function efficiently in delivering oxygen and nutrients to the tissues during continuous physical activity. A high level of cardiovascular fitness is not necessary to achieve optimum health. Research shows that people with a level of cardiovascular fitness in the lowest 20% of the population are at the highest risk for health problems. A person who simply achieves a level of cardiovascular fitness above the lower 20% of the population decreases his health risk substantially. To achieve a healthy level of cardiovascular fitness, one needs to fall within a range of 20 to 80% of the population. *FITNESSGRAM/ACTIVITYGRAM* includes scores on the PACER and one-mile run that represent healthy levels of cardiovascular fitness for youth: for example, a score on the one-mile run ranging from eight minutes and thirty seconds to eleven minutes is considered healthy for eleven-year old boys. The *FITNESSGRAM/ACTIVITYGRAM* manual contains healthy standards for cardiovascular fitness for youth aged ten to seventeen.

3. ***What are the benefits of a healthy level of cardiovascular fitness?*** A healthy level of cardiovascular fitness has two major health benefits. A healthy level of cardiovascular fitness reduces one's risk of obesity, type 2 diabetes, coronary heart disease, stroke, hypertension, and some cancers. It also increases one's ability to participate regularly in moderate to vigorous physical activity.

4. ***What are the major muscles that are affected by cardiovascular fitness activities?*** The heart is the primary muscle that is strengthened by cardiovascular fitness activities.

The other muscles that are affected by cardiovascular fitness activities depend upon the particular activity performed. For example, jogging increases the strength and endurance of the quadriceps, hamstring, and gastrocnemius muscles. In addition to the previously stated leg muscles, swimming increases the strength and endurance of the bicep, triceps, deltoid, and pectoral muscles. Appendix 1 illustrates the location of major muscles in the body.

♥ **The Hamstring muscles** are located on the back of the upper part of the leg. They received their name because butchers used to hang pigs up by these muscles!

♥ **The Gastrocnemius muscle**, also referred to as the calf muscle, is located on the back of the lower leg.

♥ **The Quadriceps** is located on the front of the leg between the hip and the knee. "Quad" means four; the quadriceps is actually four separate muscles!

5. **What is the difference between cardiovascular fitness activities for children and those for adults?** Children prefer intermittent activities where there is frequent starting and stopping while adults are more likely to choose to participate in non-stop activity. Cardiovascular activities for children, therefore, encourage students to participate continuously for longer and longer time periods during which brief periods of rest are interspersed. Asking children to perform non-stop activities may result in negative attitudes toward participation in physical activity.

6. **What are some cardiovascular fitness activities that can be performed outside the school setting?** Many of the following cardiovascular fitness activities can be performed outside of school: walking, jogging, ice skating, in-line and roller skating, skate boarding, cycling, hiking, swimming, dancing, cross-country skiing, and rowing.

7. **What are the FIT Guidelines for cardiovascular fitness for adults (see Chapter 4)?**

   F = Frequency. Perform moderate to vigorous activity (MVPA) four to six days per week.

   I = Intensity. Elevate the heart rate to within the THR while participating in MVPA.

   T = Time. Participate in non-stop MVPA for 30 to 60minutes.

   T = Type. Participate in activities that involve large muscle movements and can be performed continuously.

8. ***What are the FITT Guidelines for cardiovascular fitness for children?*** The developmental needs of children are not consistent with specialized training; thus, the guidelines for children do not include the same amounts of continuous, non-stop MVPA activity recommended for adults. The developmental needs of children necessitate intermittent breaks. The NASPE (2004) physical activity guidelines for children aged 5 to 12 are listed in Table 11.1.

Table 11.1   Physical activity guidelines for children aged 5 to 12

Physical Activity Guidelines for Children
1. Children should accumulate at least 60 minutes, and up to several hours, of age-appropriate physical activity on most if not all days of the week. This daily accumulation should include moderate and vigorous physical activity with the majority of the time being spent in activity that is intermittent in nature.
2. Children should participate in several bouts of physical activity lasting 15 minutes or more each day.
3. Children should participate each day in a variety of age appropriate physical activities designed to achieve optimal health, wellness, fitness, and performance benefits.
4. Extended periods of inactivity (periods of two or more hours) are discouraged for children, especially during the daytime hours.

9. ***What happens when a person smokes?***
- ♥ Nicotine causes an immediate increase in blood pressure, heart rate, and the flow of blood from the heart.
- ♥ Nicotine also causes the arteries to narrow.
- ♥ Carbon monoxide reduces the amount of oxygen the blood can carry.
- ♥ An imbalance in the demand for oxygen by the cells and the amount of oxygen the blood is able to supply, is created.
- ♥ Smoking further increases the amount of fatty acids, glucose, and various hormones in the blood.

The "Why" of Cardiovascular Fitness

Why is it good to "play" up a sweat? Sweating is one way the body cools itself off. Sweating may indicate the body is working hard enough to get stronger.

The "How's" of Cardiovascular Fitness

1. **How is cardiovascular fitness developed and maintained?** Healthy levels of cardiovascular fitness are developed and maintained through MVPA carried out three to four days per week. Many adults participate in activities such as walking, jogging, swimming, and cycling for cardiovascular fitness. Participation in theses and other activities (such as the activities designed for youth contained in this chapter) may positively affect cardiovascular fitness levels of children.

2. *How do the principles of exercise apply to cardiovascular fitness?*

♥ **Overload.** Increase the intensity, or time of MVPA to improve cardiovascular fitness.

♥ **Progression.** Cardiovascular fitness activities for children do start out as non-stop; they consist of brief periods of activity (approximately seven to ten seconds) interspersed with brief periods of rest (seven to ten seconds) over a period of two to three minutes. Gradually increase the time exercising, while, at the same time, decreasing (but maintaining) the resting intervals. Figure 11.4 provides a sample progression.

♥ **Specificity.** Perform MVPA within one's target heart rate range. Exercises aimed at increasing flexibility, muscular strength, or muscular endurance will have little effect upon cardiovascular fitness.

♥ **Regularity.** Perform MVPA three to four days per week. It is recommended that no more than two days elapse between workouts.

♥ **Individual Differences.** Every person is unique due to differences in body fat, nutrition, health, motivation, and genetic make-up. Do not compare students' levels' of cardiovascular fitness; encourage each child to exercise at her own pace and to achieve a level of cardiovascular fitness within the Healthy Fitness Zone.

3. *How does cigarette smoking increase one's heart attack risk?*

♥ Carbon monoxide may damage the inner walls of the arteries; this may increase the buildup of fat on these walls. Over time, this causes the vessels to narrow and harden. Nicotine may also contribute to this process.

♥ Smoking causes several changes in the blood including: increased adhesiveness and clustering of platelets in the blood, shortened platelet survival, decreased clotting time, and increased thickness of the blood.

♥ People who smoke a pack of cigarettes a day have more than twice the risk; people who smoke more than a pack a day is three times greater than people who have never smoked. Also, the earlier a person starts smoking, the greater one's risk of heart attack.

4. *How is cardiovascular fitness measured?* FITNESSGRAM/ACTIVITYGRAM includes the PACER and the one-mile run to measure cardiovascular fitness.

The "What's" of the Heart

1. ***What is the function of the heart muscle?***
   ♥ The heart pumps blood that supplies the cells of the body with fuel for energy and cleans up the waste products.

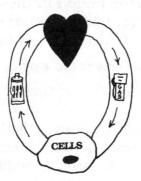

   ♥ The heart pumps five to six thousand quarts of blood every 12 hours!
   ♥ The heart never rests! It beats an average of 120,000 times each day.

2. ***What is the location of the heart?*** The heart is located just left of the middle of the chest.

3. ***What is the shape of the heart?*** The heart is shaped more like a pear than a valentine.

4. ***What is the pulse?*** The pulse is the rush of the blood through the arteries after each heartbeat; it may be found on the wrist or on the carotid artery of the neck. The index or middle finger, or both, are used to take the pulse. The heart rate may not be accurate if the thumb is used; the thumb has a pulse of its own. If too much pressure is applied when taking a pulse, it may slow down.

5. ***What is the resting heart rate (RHR)?*** The resting heart rate is the number of times the heart beats in one minute when the body is completely relaxed. A good time to take the RHR is in the morning while still lying in bed. A child's resting heart rate may range from 60 to 95 beats per minute.

6. ***What is the maximum heart rate (MHR)?*** The maximum heart rate is the maximum number of times the heart can beat in one minute. At birth, the MHR is approximately 220 beats per minute. Each year after birth, the MHR drops approximately one beat per year. The MHR is estimated to be 220 minus a person's age in years. For example, a 10-year-old's MHR is approximately 210 beats per minute.

    If a person runs at top speed for 10 seconds, as in a 100-yard dash, her heart rate would probably reach its maximum. A person cannot exercise for very long at her maximum heart rate.

7. ***What is the target heart rate range (THR)?*** The target heart rate range is the number of times the heart needs to beat in one minute during activity to improve cardiovascular fitness. Benefits will be minimal if one does not elevate his heart rate to the THR range during cardiovascular fitness activity. One's THR range is 60% to 85% of her MHR. Figure 11.2 shows the calculation of a 10-year-old's target heart rate range.

Figure 11.2 Calculation of target heart rate for a 10-year old

Target Heart Rate Range for a 10-year old

60% of MHR =   210
              x   .60
                     126   **Target Heart Rate Range**
                                  126 to 179 beats per minute

85% of MHR =   210
              x   .85
                     178.5

8. ***What is the 10-second target heart rate?*** Take the target heart rate for 10 seconds immediately after stopping exercise; the heart rate will slow down too much if it is taken for an entire minute. The THR range for a 10-second pulse is calculated by dividing the one-minute THR range by 6 (Figure 11.3).

Figure 11.3 Calculating the 10-second THR range for a 10-year old

10 Second Target Heart Rate Range for a 10-year old

```
        21                          29.8
  6 | 126                      6 | 179.0
      12                           12
      06                           59
      06                           54
       0                           50
```

The 10-second target heart rate range for a 10-year-old is 21 to 30 (29.8 is rounded to 30) beats in 10 seconds. Figure 11.4 presents the MHR, THR range, and 10-second THR range calculations for ages five to sixty.

Figure 11.4   MHR and 10-second THR ranges for people ages 5-60

Maximum Heart Rate and
Target Heart Rate Range: 10 Second Count

AGES 5 to 60

Age	Maximum Heart Rate Beats Per Minute (220 – age)	Target Heart Rate Range 10-Second Count					
		60%	65%	70%	75%	80%	85%
5	215	22	23	25	27	29	31
6	214	21	23	25	27	29	30
7	213	21	23	25	27	28	30
8	212	21	23	25	27	28	30
9	211	21	23	25	26	28	30
10	210	21	23	25	26	28	30
11	209	21	23	24	26	28	30
12	208	21	23	24	26	28	29
13	207	21	22	24	26	28	29
14	206	21	22	24	26	27	29
15	205	21	22	24	26	27	29
16	204	20	22	24	26	27	29
17	203	20	22	24	26	27	29
18	202	20	22	24	25	27	29
19	201	20	22	23	25	27	29
20	200	20	22	23	25	27	28
21	199	20	22	23	25	27	28
22	198	20	21	23	25	27	28
23	197	20	21	23	25	26	28
24	196	20	21	23	25	26	28
25	195	20	21	23	24	26	28
30	190	19	21	22	24	25	27
35	185	19	20	22	24	25	27
40	180	18	20	22	23	25	26
45	175	18	19	21	23	24	25
50	170	17	18	20	21	23	24
55	165	17	18	20	21	22	23
60	160	16	17	19	20	21	23

The "Why's" of the Heart

1. ***Why is cardiovascular fitness important for the heart muscle?***
   Cardiovascular fitness activities help the heart, the most important muscle in the body, to become stronger.

2. ***Why is a strong heart important?***

♥   A stronger heart muscle is able to pump more blood with each beat. When the heart is able to pump more blood with each beat, it does not have to beat as many times in the long run. The amount of blood pumped with each beat is called the stroke volume.

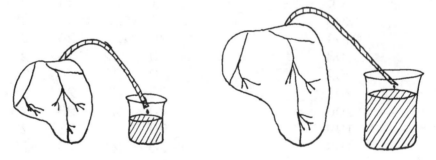

♥   A strong heart muscle will last longer than a weak heart muscle. The heart is like a car; keep it "tuned up" and get extra mileage out of it!

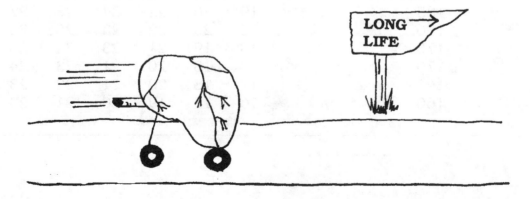

The "How's" of the Heart

1. ***How does the heart become stronger?*** When the heart beats faster during cardiovascular fitness activities (continuous at one's target heart rate), the heart muscle is becoming stronger. The heart is a muscle like the bicep is a muscle. The bicep muscle is a good example to use for comparison, because the students can see and feel the biceps when they contract the biceps like Popeye!

The more we use or exercise the biceps, the stronger the biceps become. Similarly, when the heart beats faster for a continuous amount of time during cardiovascular fitness activities, it becomes stronger.

2. ***How big is the heart?*** A person's heart is the size of his fist; however, not all hearts are the same size.

♥   A mouse's heart is the size of a raspberry!

♥   A rabbit's heart is the size of an egg!

♥   A Collie's heart is the size of a tennis ball!

♥   A giraffe's heart is the size of a basketball!

The "What's" of the Lungs

1. *What are the lungs?* The lungs are two pinkish air sacks located inside of the chest. Breathing in deeply causes the chest to expand; like a balloon, the chest takes up more room when it is filled with air!

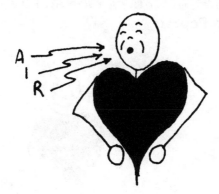

2. *What does aerobic mean?* Aerobic means "with oxygen." Cardiovascular fitness activities are aerobic; they require oxygen for energy.

3. *What does anaerobic mean?* Anaerobic means "without air." Anaerobic activities rely on chemical reactions inside the body to provide short bursts of energy for the muscles during activity. Intermittent activities that do not require oxygen for energy are called anaerobic; any vigorous activity lasting less than two to three minutes is probably anaerobic. An example of an anaerobic activity is the 50-yard dash. Many popular sports are anaerobic.

♥ The average play in football lasts four to ten seconds!
♥ Short bursts of energy are needed to run the bases or field a ball in baseball and softball.

The "Why's" of the Lungs

1. *Why is breathing important during activity?* Breathing deeply while physically active insures that an adequate amount of oxygen is absorbed into the blood.

2. *Why does a side ache occur?* A side ache is caused by the cramping of the diaphragm muscle located underneath the lungs. Inhaling (breathing in) more air (oxygen), may help eliminate the side ache.

The "How's" of the Lungs

1. ***How does air cycle through the lungs?*** Air contains oxygen. Oxygen is the energy or fuel for the muscles. Just as a car needs gas to keep moving, the muscles need oxygen!

♥ The blood picks up the oxygen from the lungs and carries it to the heart. The heart pumps the oxygen-rich blood to the muscles of the body. Oxygen-rich blood is bright red in color.

♥ The blood carries the oxygen to the muscles where it is used for energy. Then the blood, depleted of oxygen and containing waste products, returns to the lungs.

♥ The blood is now dark red in color because it no longer contains oxygen. It carries carbon dioxide (a waste product) to the lungs where it is exhaled from the body.

♥ The blood then picks up a fresh supply of oxygen, returning it to its bright red color, to be delivered to the muscles.

2. ***How does smoking affect the lungs?*** Smoking increases one's risk of emphysema and lung cancer. Non-smokers live an average of seven years longer than smokers.

The "What's" of Blood Vessels

1. ***What are blood vessels?*** Blood vessels are flexible tubes that carry the blood, pumped by the heart, to all areas of the body. The body has over 60,000 miles of blood vessels! Four major vessels are the arteries, arterioles, capillaries, and veins. (Learn how the blood circulates through the body under "The How's of the Lungs" section.)

2. ***What is atherosclerosis?*** Atherosclerosis is a build-up of fatty deposits on the inner wall of the arteries. These deposits narrow the blood vessels; the heart has to work harder to pump blood through the narrowed blood vessels.

3. ***What is the composition of blood?*** Blood is composed of plasma, red blood cells, white blood cells, and platelets.

♥   **Plasma** is a yellowish liquid when it is separated from the blood cells. It is 90% water, but also contains protein, fat, sugar, and other materials. One of the functions of plasma is to provide the blood cells with a medium in which they may move.

♥   **Red blood cells** are shaped a little bit like doughnuts. Their main function is to pick up oxygen from the lungs and deliver it to the cells of the body. There are about 30 trillion (30,000,000,000,000!) red blood cells in the body!

♥   **White blood cells** are two to three times larger than red blood cells; however, there are not as many of them. White blood cells fight germs and infection. When sick or injured, the body will automatically create more white blood cells to help speed up recovery!

♥   **Platelets** function to clot the blood. Blood clotting helps stop bleeding when the body is cut or scraped.

The "Why" of Blood Vessels

Why is cardiovascular fitness activity important for the blood vessels?
Cardiovascular fitness activity may increase the diameter of the blood vessels. The blood vessels may become stronger and more flexible as a result of the continuous increased heart rate, and subsequent increased blood flow, during activity.

The "How's" of Blood Vessels

1. *How does blood circulate through the body?*

♥ Arteries take blood from the heart; they stretch and squeeze the blood into smaller vessels.

♥ The smaller blood vessels, arterioles, carry blood to the capillaries.

♥ The capillaries are very thin and nearly invisible. The fuel from the blood squeezes through the tiny walls of the capillaries into the cells of the body.

♥ Cells are tiny factories. They are the building blocks of the body. After the fuel is used as energy by the cells, waste products are created. These waste products are then sent to the veins by way of the capillaries.

♥ Veins are tubes that carry the oxygen-depleted blood (filled with waste products) back to the heart. Most of the oxygen-depleted blood must travel "uphill" (against gravity) to return to the heart. To prevent the blood from pooling in the hands and feet, the veins have one-way valves that close after the blood passes through. These valves insure that the blood does not flow "downhill" back to the cells. The use of one-way valves to return oxygen-depleted blood to the heart is called venous return.

2. *How does physical activity affect circulation of blood through the heart?* The heart muscle has arteries called coronary arteries. Regular participation in cardiovascular fitness activity will help open up coronary arteries so the heart does not need to work as hard to pump the blood.

3. *How does atherosclerosis relate to heart attacks and strokes?* Atherosclerosis is the major cause of heart attack and stroke. The arteries get so clogged with fatty deposits that they close up and won't permit the blood to flow through. Fatty deposits can become so large that they close the blood vessels completely, or a blood clot can form on the rough surface of the fatty deposit that can block the artery. When this happens to an artery within the heart (a coronary artery), a heart attack occurs. When it happens to an artery that supplies blood to the brain, a stroke occurs.

The concepts presented in this chapter provide teachers with a starting point for educating students about cardiovascular fitness. The American Heart Association and other local, state and national organizations offer extensive material related to the heart and the importance of regular participation in physical activity (see websites at the end of this chapter).

CARDIOVASCULAR FITNESS ACTIVITIES

This section contains the following cardiovascular fitness activities that are designed to be fun and to provide experiences through which students develop feelings of confidence and competence. The process of participation in these activities is more important than the product of a healthy level of cardiovascular fitness.

1. Power Walking with Pedometers
2. Locomotor Movements
3. Parachute Fitness
4. Rhythmic Aerobics
5. Walk, Jog, Sprint
6. Four-Corners Movement
7. Astronaut Drills
8. Jump Rope Fitness
9. Circuit Training
10. Jogging
11. Continuity Activity
12. New Leader Activity
13. Challenge Courses
14. Squad Leader Activity
15. PACER

For each of activities, the following information is provided.

♥ Description
♥ Organization
♥ Sample beginning activity
♥ Variations

The activities in this chapter are designed to elevate the heart rate for a continuous period of time. At the beginning of the school year, short periods of activity are interspersed with rest. Gradually, the time of activity increases and the resting time decreases. A recommended one-year time progression for cardiovascular fitness activities is presented in Figure 11.4. The progression is only a suggestion; progressing too fast may discourage students while progressing too slow will result in boredom.

If fitness levels are low, the activity is stopped often; during the rest periods, the students practice feeling their pulse and discuss fitness concepts. It is not necessary for students to obtain an accurate count of their pulse. It is more important that they know how and where to find the pulse and that they are able to feel that the pulse is faster after activity than it is at rest. Eventually, as fitness levels increase, the students participate in non-stop activity for longer periods of time and with fewer and shorter rest periods.

Cardiovascular fitness activities are fun! Modeling by the teacher will motivate students; the teacher can exaggerate the correct form of the movements. The more the students enjoy the activities, the more likely they will be to continue participating regularly in physical activity on their own! The ☐ sign identifies guidelines for performing certain activities correctly.

Figure 11.4 A recommended one-year time progression for cardiovascular fitness activities

Cardiovascular Fitness Progression

Use the following progression for cardiovascular fitness activities with students at a low fitness level. The purpose of this progression is to insure that students are not asked to do too much too soon; cardiovascular fitness activities are fun and develop feelings of competence and confidence. Make modifications depending on students' fitness levels. Intermittent periods of rest are recommended, even as students' levels of fitness increase.

Week 1	Activities last a total of 1 to 3 minutes. Stop activity every 15 seconds. Students feel their pulse and concepts are discussed during 15-second rest periods.
Weeks 2 to 4	Activities last a total of 2 to 3 minutes. Stop for 15-second rest periods every 15 to 20 seconds.
Weeks 5 to 7	Activities last from 2 to 4 minutes. Stop for 10-second rest periods every 20 to 25 seconds.
Weeks 8 to 10	Activities last from 3 to 5 minutes. Stop for 10-second rest periods every 25 to 30 seconds.
Weeks 11 to 13	Activities last from 5 to 6 minutes. Stop for 10-second rest periods every 30 to 35 seconds.
Weeks 14 to 16	Activities last from 6 to 7 minutes. Stop for 7-second rest periods every 35 to 40 seconds.
Weeks 17 to 19	Activities last from 7 to 8 minutes. Stop for 7-second rest periods every 40 to 45 seconds.
Weeks 20 to 22	Activities last from 8 to 9 minutes. Stop for 7-second rest periods every 45 to 50 seconds.
Weeks 23 to 25	Activities last from 9 to 10 minutes. Stop for 5-second rest periods every 50 to 55 seconds.
Weeks 26 to 28	Activities last from 10 to 11 minutes. Stop for 5-second rest periods every 60 to 65 seconds.
Weeks 29 to 31	Activities last from 11 to 12 minutes. Stop for 5-second rest periods every 65 to 70 seconds.
Weeks 32 to 34	Activities last from 12 to 13 minutes. Stop for 5-second rest periods every 70 to 75 seconds.

1. POWER WALKING WITH PEDOMETERS

Description

Power walking, a popular cardiovascular fitness activity among adults, is also enjoyable for children. Walking, because it is low impact and requires no skills in addition to walking, is the best activity for overweight children and anyone who desires to participate in low impact activity. Teachers are encouraged to allow power walking as a substitute option for any of the activities in this chapter. For example, during locomotor movements, a child who cannot do participate in high impact movements like running and hopping, may be given the option to power walk while the other students perform these activities. Additionally, a child who may not be able to jump rope (or learn to jump rope) due to a minor injury or being overweight, can choose to power walk within boundaries set up adjacent to the rope jumping activity.

Power walking is simply a brisk walk with exaggerated arm swings. Proper walking form prevents injuries from occurring due to improper technique. To power walk correctly:

√   Relax the shoulders, arms, and hands.

√   Swing the arms until the wrist reaches shoulder level.

√   Walk with a heel to toe motion with one foot always in contact with the ground.

√   Try to walk as fast as possible, with a smooth, even stride.

Power walking can be taught with or without pedometers; however, teachers are encouraged to purchase a class set of pedometers per grade level (see chapter 4 and Appendix 3 for more information on pedometers). Pedometers can be used not only in power walking but in most of the cardiovascular fitness activities included in this chapter. [See *Pedometer Power* by Pangrazi, Beighle, & Sidman (2003) for a variety of lesson ideas utilizing pedometers.] Teachers are encouraged to incorporate the use pedometers throughout the physical education program to empower students to participate in adequate amounts of physical activity.

Pedometers

Pedometers are a small (approximately 2" X 2") electronic device used to measure the number of steps a person takes. There are numerous types of pedometers that vary significantly in function and price. The most basic pedometer simply measures steps; in fact, at one time McDonalds gave away free pedometers with an adult Happy Meal! Based upon a few user's reports, however, these did not work for long! (See Appendix 3 for pedometer websites.) Pedometers are appropriate for use during power walking at a brisk, even stride. While they are less accurate when one walks slowly or with an uneven gait, they can still be used to obtain an approximate estimate of steps taken. They cannot, however, provide any measurements for swimming, cycling or any kind of skating or skate boarding.

How to Use Pedometers to Count Steps. Students place their pedometer on their waistband, directly above the hip bone (in line with ankle and knee). To determine accuracy, students reset the steps to 0, close the pedometer (it will not count steps while open), and take twenty-five steps. After taking forty steps, students open the pedometer (without taking it off the waistband) and scroll to "steps." The pedometer is considered accurate if the number of steps recorded is within three (over or under) of the actual steps taken.

How to Use Pedometers to Determine Distance Covered and Calories Expended. In addition to measuring steps, some pedometers also calculate distance covered and calories burned. The calculation of distance covered and calories burned requires the user to enter stride length and weight, respectively, into the pedometer. To help students' determine stride their individual stride length, the teacher marks a 10 foot distance. The student counts her steps as she covers the distance; she then divides the number of steps into 10. For example, if a student takes 6 steps to cover the 10' distance, her stride length is 10/6 or 1.66 feet per stride. Most pedometers require the user to enter stride length in .25 foot increments (e.g. 1, 1.25, 1.5, 1.75, 2.0) up to a maximum of six feet. Thus, a student with a stride length of 1.66 feet, could choose to enter either 1.5 feet or 1.75 feet.

Organization
Organize power walking in one of two ways; students walk randomly within large boundaries, or students walk around a designated course or trail.

Sample Beginning Activity: Power Walking
1. Students feel their pulse before starting activity
2. Power walk for 15 to 20 seconds.
3. Stop and feel pulse
4. Continue power walking. The speed is modified to match fitness levels. A beginning power walking activities lasts two to 10 minutes with periods of walking interspersed with rest. During rest periods students open pedometers (without removing from waistband) to view number of steps.
5. Students can keep a log of steps taken and set goals for increasing steps.
6. As students become more experienced with pedometers, they can wait until the end of an activity to view steps.

Variations
1. Students can record steps during a sequence of lessons and set new goals each day.
2. Students can set a goal of walking to a specific location. They can record their distance each day, total it individually or as a class, and measure progress toward reaching the location.
3. Students can record daily calories burned and compare calories burned with calories in their favorite foods (See Chapter 12 for specific information on reading nutrition labels).

2. LOCOMOTOR MOVEMENTS

This locomotor movement activity is most appropriate for use at the beginning of the school year. Not only does this activity provide the foundation for the basic movements, it provides an ideal opportunity to introduce and reinforce key safety precautions that apply to all physical education lessons. In this lesson, students learn to make eye contact to avoid collisions and to stop with their legs apart and knees bent to avoid falling.

Description

Students move continuously using the eight fundamental locomotor movements. These movements are, in order of progression: walking, running, jumping, hopping, skipping, galloping, sliding, and leaping. A walk is characterized by the feet moving forward alternately, one step at a time. One foot is always in contact with the ground. A run is a movement where, for a brief moment, both feet are off the ground. In jumping, the body is lifted into the air by pushing off and landing with both feet. A hop is similar to a jump, however, only one foot is used to take off and land. A skip is a series on continuous step-hops. When galloping, the lead foot moves out in a forward direction and the other follows; the back leg tries to catch up with the front leg, but it never does! A slide is the same movement as the gallop except the movement is to the side. A leap is an elongated step in which one pushes off with one leg and lands on the other. Running and leaping are usually combined.

WALK   RUN   JUMP   HOP

SKIP   GALLOP   SLIDE   LEAP

Organization

Mark the boundaries for this activity with eight or more cones (Twelve to 24 cones are recommended for grades K-3!). Boundaries are large enough so that the students are not crowded. A scattered formation is recommended. Popular music, pre-recorded on a cassette tape or CD and played in the background, motivates students and makes the activity more fun!

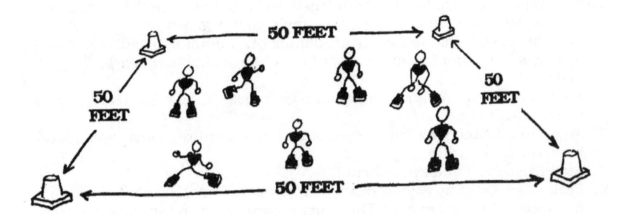

Stress proper form when teaching locomotor activities. For example, when students are walking, their heads are up, shoulders back, and hands out of pockets.

When students are moving within the boundaries, they are instructed to make eye contact with each other to avoid collisions and stop with their legs apart, knees bent for balance. Practice stopping with a low center of gravity and bent knees for stability. Emphasize listening skills during locomotor movement activities; students practice stopping immediately when the signal is given.

For Kindergarten through third grade, the eight locomotor movements may be split into two lessons. The first four movements are repeated two or three times on the first day. On the second day, the first four locomotor movements are reviewed and the remaining four are introduced. An example of how to incorporate concepts has been included in this activity.

Sample Beginning Activity: Locomotor Movements

1. Students feel their pulse before starting activity. Do not count beats, just become aware of the rate of the heart beat.
2. Walk in all directions: fast, slow, high, low! Head up, shoulders back, hands out of pockets. make eye contact with other students; change direction if you get close to another person (make eye contact and change direction during all locomotor movement activities). Avoid collisions!!
3. Stop on signal from teacher with legs apart and knees bent for balance (stop in this position each time the stop signal is given).
4. Feel Pulse. Q. "What is your heart doing?" A. "Pumping blood!"
5. Run in all directions (make eye contact, change direction): slow, fast, faster!
6. Stop (legs apart and knees bent) and feel pulse. Q. "Is your heart beating faster?" A. "Yes."
7. Jump in all directions (make eye contact, change directions): quiet, loud, forward, backward!
8. Stop (legs apart and knees bent)!
9. Feel pulse. Q. "Why is your heart beating faster?" A. "Because exercising muscles need more energy. The heart pumps the blood that carries the oxygen to the muscles for energy."
10. Hop in all directions (make eye contact, change directions): circle, square, change feet.
11. Stop (legs apart and knees bent) and feel pulse. Q. "What is the most important muscle in the body?" A. "The heart."
12. Skip in all directions (make eye contact, change directions): high, low, swing arms!
13. Stop (legs apart and knees bent) and feel pulse. Q. "How big is the heart?" A. "It is the size of the fist." Have students hold their fists in the air.
14. Gallop in all directions (make eye contact, change directions): forward, backward, change lead leg, spank your horse!
15. Stop (legs apart and knees bent) and feel pulse. Students open and close their fists to the beat of their hearts.
16. Slide in all directions (make eye contact, change directions): fast, slow, bend knees low, hands out, arms out like a basketball player!
17. Stop (legs apart and knees bent) and feel pulse.
18. Leap in all directions (make eye contact, change directions): high, far!
19. Stop (legs apart and knees bent) and feel pulse.

Variations

Animal Walks. Incorporate animal movements into this activity for grades kindergarten through three. Chapter 13 contains descriptions of animal walks.

Add Equipment. Use equipment such as playground balls, hoops, bean bags, balloons, and beach balls during the activity.

3. PARACHUTE FITNESS

Description

Students use the parachute in continuous activity. Many movement patterns can be performed while holding the parachute or while the parachute is spread out on the ground. Use music during the parachute activity. The movement pattern is changed every eight or sixteen counts.

The amount of time spent performing each of the activity depends upon the fitness levels of the students. Periods of rest are inserted every 15 to 30 seconds if this activity is used early in the year. Feel the pulse and discuss concepts during the rest periods.

Organization

Students space themselves evenly around the parachute. For a class of 25 to 35 students, a parachute measuring 24 to 30 feet in diameter is appropriate.

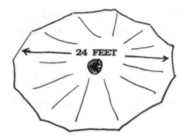

Teamwork is necessary because students perform movements at the same time, as well as move at the same speed during parachute activities. If one student runs over the student next to her, the entire class will be in a heap in three seconds!

Sample Beginning Activity: Parachute Fitness

1. Feel pulse before starting activity.
2. March in place while holding the parachute waist high. Do not let the parachute sag!
3. Continue to jog in place and begin to "shake the rug" by making small, fast, up and down movements with the parachute.
4. Hold the parachute up high while marching in place.
5. Hold the parachute with the left hand and walk or jog in a counterclockwise direction.

6. Change direction. Hold the parachute with the right hand and walk or jog in a clockwise direction.

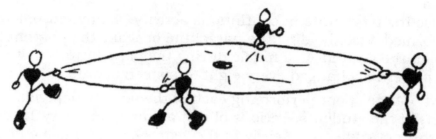

7. Hold the parachute with both hands and slide to the right or counterclockwise.
8. Slide to the left or clockwise.
9. Place the parachute on the ground and skip around it to the right.
10. Skip to the left.
11. Stop, drop the parachute, and perform jumping jacks.
12. Grab the parachute with both hands and shake it while jogging in place.
13. Feel pulse.

Variation
Teach a routine to music. The following is a sample beginning rhythmic routine to music.

1. Shake the parachute for 16 counts.
2. Hold the parachute with the right hand and walk clockwise for 16 counts.
3. Change directions and walk holding the parachute with the left hand for 16 counts.
4. Stop and shake the parachute for 16 counts.
5. Raise the parachute overhead for eight counts.
6. Keep the parachute taut and lower it to the ground for eight counts.
7. Raise it overhead in eight counts.
8. Lower it to the ground in eight counts.
9. Repeat from the beginning

Start with a simple activity involving little explanation. If the activity is complex, the emphasis will change from continuous movement to stopping and starting while new movements are practiced. Start simple and build slowly!

4. RHYTHMIC AEROBICS

Description
Students move continuously using rhythmic movement patterns. This method of developing cardiovascular fitness is very popular among adults and can be easily adapted for children. Many people refer to these movements as "aerobic dance" or "aerobics."

At the beginning of the program, hold frequent rest periods during which students feel their pulse and concepts are discussed. Eventually, continue the activities non-stop for several minutes. Teach students the difference between high impact and low impact movements. Both feet leave the ground simultaneously during high impact movements. High impact movements, such as jumping jacks, can be modified to low impact movements by performing them with one foot in constant contact with the ground. Make a tape alternating 10 seconds of music (for movement) with 10 to 15 seconds of silence (for feeling the pulse and for discussing concepts).

Organization
Arrange students in a scattered formation. Establish boundaries are large enough for students to move without bumping into each other. Teach simple movements such as jogging in place with high knees, jump and clap, and jump and kick. Complicated movements and dance steps may discourage students and be time consuming to teach.

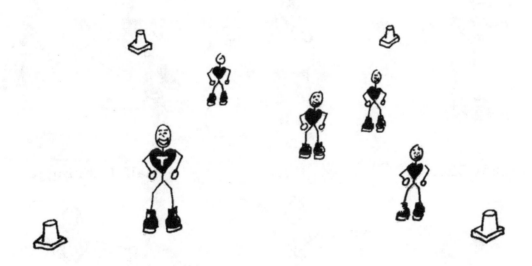

Sample Beginning Activity: Rhythmic Aerobics
1. Students feel their pulse before starting activity.
2. Jump and clap for 10 seconds.
3. Stop and feel pulse.
4. Jog in place and clap hands for 15 seconds.
5. Stop and feel pulse.
6. Add simple rhythmic movements interspersed with stopping and feeling the pulse.

Suggested movements

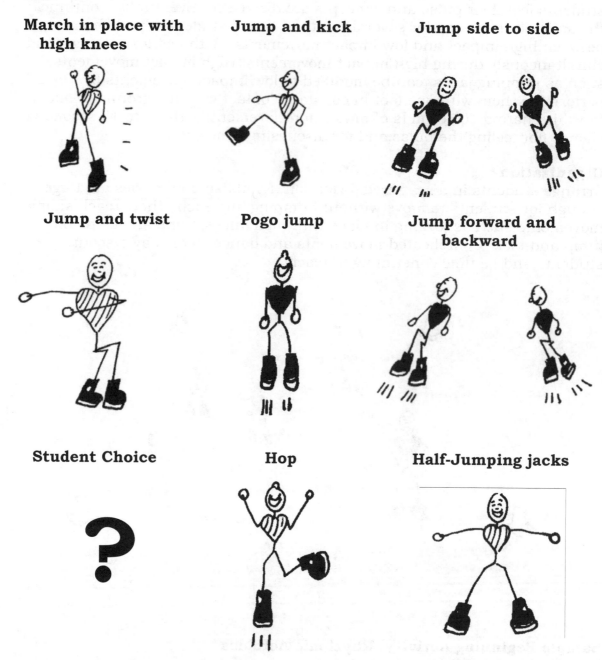

March in place with high knees

Jump and kick

Jump side to side

Jump and twist

Pogo jump

Jump forward and backward

Student Choice

Hop

Half-Jumping jacks

7. Feel pulse.

√   Land on the soles of the feet. Landing on the balls of the feet may lead to injury. Alternate high impact movements, such as jumping jacks, with low impact movements such as marching in place. Encourage students to modify activities according to their fitness levels.

Variations

Jump Ropes. Each student has a jump rope and lays it out on the ground. The students can jump back and forth over the rope or they can pick it up and jump for short periods.

Balls. Each student bounces a ball while exercising. Additionally, a ball (or a hat, flag, beanbag) is used to designate the person who is leading; the students pass the ball to each other or the teacher takes the ball from the leader and gives it to a new student.

Balloons. Keep one or more balloons (or beach balls) up in the air during the activity.

5. WALK, JOG, SPRINT

Description

Students move continuously in all directions, walking, jogging, and sprinting on signals from the teacher.

Organization

Students move in a scattered formation within or around boundaries. Use a whistle, tambourine, or other instrument to signal changes in movement: one signal to walk, two signals to jog, and three signals to sprint. Spend more time jogging and sprinting than walking as the fitness levels of the students increase.

Sample Beginning Activity: Walk, Jog, and Sprint

1. Students feel their pulse before starting activity.
2. Walk for 20 seconds.
3. Jog for 15 seconds.
4. Sprint for five seconds.
5. Stop and feel pulse.
6. Jog for 10 seconds.
7. Walk for 15 seconds.
8. Jog for 10 seconds.
9. Sprint for five seconds.
10. Stop and feel pulse.

Variations

Run, Skip, Gallop. Use a variety of combinations of locomotor movements.

Wind Sprints. Students sprint for a short distance followed by equal distances of walking or jogging. Place boundary markers on the field to mark the point at which the students sprint walk or jog.

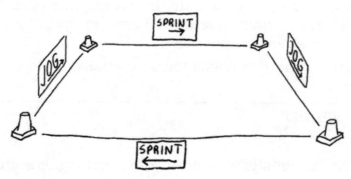

Secret Code. Use cones to designate changes in locomotor movements. One cone signals walking, two cones signal jogging, three cones signal sprinting.

---

6. FOUR-CORNERS MOVEMENT

Description

Students move continuously around the outside of a large square area, changing the method of locomotion each time a corner is turned.

Organization

Place four cones in a square; each side of the square is approximately 20 feet long. Place a poster board sign against each cone designating the method of locomotion to be performed in moving to the next corner of the square. Students move continuously around the boundaries while the music plays; they walk when the music stops. Designate a passing lane around the outside of the course; if a student wants to pass someone, he passes to the outside. Encourage students to participate at their own rate.

Sample Beginning Activity: Four Corners Movement
1. Students feel their pulse before starting activity.
2. Students move from cone to cone (around the outside) for 10 seconds performing the movements named on the signs.
3. After 10 seconds of movement, the students walk and feel their pulse.
4. Resume Four-Corners. Follow the above procedure for a total of seven, ten-second periods.

Suggested movements

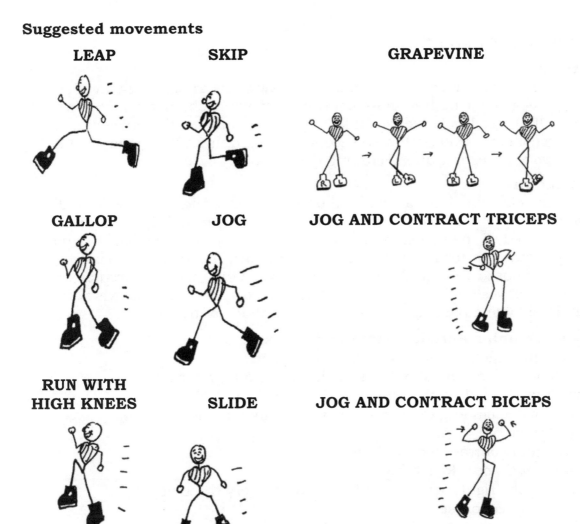

LEAP   **SKIP**   **GRAPEVINE**

GALLOP   **JOG**   **JOG AND CONTRACT TRICEPS**

RUN WITH HIGH KNEES   **SLIDE**   **JOG AND CONTRACT BICEPS**

Variations

Three part sign. List three movements on each sign. Each time the students pass the same sign, they perform the next movement listed. After performing the third movement, they repeat the first.

Six or eight-corners movement. Use additional signs to create five or six corners.

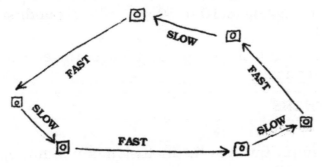

Interspersed jogging. Break up the activity by jogging. For example, on a signal, the students jog in the same (or opposite) direction of Four-Corners Movement. Use a different song to signal jogging.

7. ASTRONAUT DRILLS

Description

A variety of locomotor and non-locomotor movements are combined with walking or jogging. Children move continuously while changing movement patterns. If fitness levels are low, take a rest period to feel the pulse and introduce concepts every 10 to 15 seconds; a beginning activity may last a total of two to three minutes including rest periods.

Organization

Arrange the class in either a scattered or a circular formation. A scattered formation is recommended for grades kindergarten through three; boundaries are established so the students are aware of the area within which they may move. A circular pattern, in which the students are spaced four to six feet apart, can be used with grades four through six. When using a circular pattern, directives such as right, left, clockwise, and counterclockwise are useful. Designate a passing lane around the outside of the circle.

Sample Beginning Activity: Astronaut Drills

1. Students feel their pulse before starting activity.
2. Walk with head up, shoulders back, hands out of pockets!
3. Walk while circling the arms forward. Giant circles!
4. Walk while circling the arms backward. Small circles!
5. Feel pulse.
6. Walk and contract biceps. Pump it up!
7. Walk on tiptoes. Reach high!
8. Hop on the right foot and left foot. Switch every three hops!
9. Stop and feel pulse.
10. Walk with tiny steps. Step as quickly as you can!
11. Walk with giant steps! Step as softly as you can!
12. Walk and clap. Clap faster!
13. Feel pulse.

Variations

Increase intensity. Substitute jogging for walking. Direct the students to jog freely within the activity area (or outside the boundaries!) periodically during the activity. Continue jogging for 10 to 60 seconds, depending upon the fitness levels of the students.

Student leaders. Use volunteers to lead portions of the activity; each student leads for 10 to 15 seconds.

8. JUMP ROPE FITNESS

Description

Jump rope fitness simply involves the inclusion of a jump rope for every child in non-stop activity. Use the rope in a variety of ways depending upon the rope jumping skills of the students; some examples follow.

1. Lay out the jump rope on the ground in a straight line or shape of the child's choice. Jump over and around it.
2. Hold both handles of the rope in one hand; turn the rope at your side while moving the feet continuously.
3. Hold one rope handle in each hand. With each turn of the rope, step or jump over it. Keep elbows in and close to the waist; use the wrists (not big arm movements) to turn the rope.

Use music in the background to make the activity more fun! If fitness levels are low, make a tape with 10-15 seconds of silence for every 10-15 seconds of music. Jump rope while the music plays and stop, feel pulse, and discuss concepts during the silence.

Organization

Establish boundaries large enough so students, when scattered within them, can use their ropes without hurting each other. Rope jumping works best on a solid surface such as blacktop; grass is not recommended as a surface for rope jumping. Each student uses a rope that is the correct length; a rope that is too long or too short may prevent a child from jumping correctly. To determine the correct length, the student stands on the rope with his feet together; when the handles are lifted, they come up to a level even with the armpits.

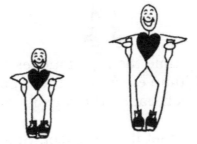

Generally:

√   Grades kindergarten through two use ropes seven feet in length.
√   Grades three through five use ropes seven to eight feet in length.
√   Grades six and up use ropes seven to ten feet in length.

Progression for Teaching Students to Jump Rope. There are usually a few students in each class who do not know how to jump rope well enough to participate in the following activities. Instruct these students hold both of the handles in one hand and turn the rope at their side while jumping; this enables them to become familiar with the rhythm of rope jumping without the frustration of stopping and starting with each missed jump! With a little extra practice, the non-jumpers in the class can become proficient in rope jumping. The following is a sample teaching progression for students who do not know how to jump rope. It is followed by a sample beginning activity for jump rope fitness.

1. Lay the rope out in a straight line.
2. Stand with the feet together just to one side of the rope.
3. Jump side to side, one jump per side, over the rope without touching it. Progress to jumping two times on each side.

4. Hold the rope with both handles in one hand, keeping the elbow of the turning arm in close to the hips.
5. Turn the rope at the side of the body. Use the wrist, not the entire arm, to turn the rope. Keep the elbows in while turning.

6. Bend the knees every time the rope touches the ground.
7. Bend the knees and jump every time the rope touches the ground.
8. Hold one handle in each hand. The rope is touching the ground behind the feet.
9. Turn the rope once and let it hit the feet. Step over it.

10. Turn the rope once; this time step over the rope as it passes under the feet. The rope does not touch the feet.
11. Jump over the rope without stopping each time it comes around.
12. Continue to practice jumping the rope one time, two times in a row, three times in a row. Add one jump each time.
13. Practice jumping slow time, two jumps per turn of the rope, and fast time, one jump per turn of the rope.

Sample Beginning Activity: Rope Jumping

1. Place the rope in a straight line on the ground.
2. Students feel their pulse before starting activity.
3. Jog around the rope. Do not touch the rope!
4. Start at one end of the rope and jump side to side to the other end.
5. Turn around and jump side to side back to the starting point.
6. Jump backwards down the length of the rope.
7. Skip around the rope.
8. Change directions and gallop around the rope.
9. Change directions and slide around the rope.
10. Pick up the rope with both handles in one hand. Turn the rope at the side of the body. Jump each time the rope touches the ground.
11. Change hands and repeat.
12. With handles still in one hand, turn the rope first on one side of the body and then on the other. (While doing this, the hand completes in a figure eight motion.) Keep elbows in.
13. With one handle in each hand, begin to jump rope slow time; jump twice for each turn of the rope. The second jump is called the rebound jump.
14. Feel pulse.
15. Jump rope while jogging. Jog around the area, turning the rope overhead and stepping over it while jogging. Make eye contact and change direction when close to others.

Variations: additional jump rope challenges

Jump fast time. Jump once for each turn of the rope.

Alternate feet. Step over the rope one foot at a time.

Hop on one foot. Switch feet every two to three hops.

Jump side to side. Alternate jumping from one side to the other.

Swing step forward. While jumping over the rope, kick one leg out forward. Alternate legs.

Cross-over step. As rope comes over head, cross arms in front of the body so one elbow is on top of the other elbow. Jump through the rope while the arms are crossed. Next time the rope comes over, uncross arms and jump. Perform the cross-over step using both slow time and fast time.

Double jump. Spin the rope twice for each single jump. Students master fast time (see above) before attempting this! Turn the rope faster and jump higher to complete a double jump!

9. CIRCUIT TRAINING

Description

Set up ten to fifteen stations (based on class size—one station for each 3 students) around the perimeter of the activity area. The students rotate from station to station and perform the activity specified at each one. The activities at each station are moderate to vigorous, non-stop movements designed to elevate the students' heart rates to the target heart rate range.

Organization

Position the stations in a circle, square, or rectangle, five to twenty feet apart. Use10 to 15 stations to insure a small number of students at each station; a maximum of four students per station is recommended.

Signs designate the specific activity to be performed at each station; use words or pictures large enough to be seen clearly from a distance of 30 feet to describe each activity.

Teach students how to perform each exercise included in the circuit before the Circuit Training activity is introduced. Assign students to a starting station. On the start signal (one whistle or music playing), activity starts. On the rotation signal (two whistles or silence), activity ceases and students rotate to the next station. On the start signal, students begin activity at their new station.

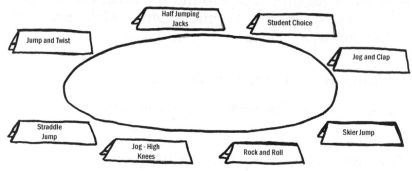

Perform activities in the circuit continuously for several seconds. The time spent exercising, and the time spent rotating to the next station, depend upon the fitness levels of the students. For a beginning level of fitness, spend approximately seven seconds exercising at each station, and allow fifteen seconds for rotation to the next station. As fitness levels increase, spend up to one minute at each station and reduce rotation time to five seconds.

A Circuit Training tape, alternating music with silence, is recommended. Students exercise while the music is playing. During each period of silence, students stop exercising and rotate to the next station. When the music resumes playing, students begin exercising. A pre-recorded tape frees the teacher to participate with the students. Circuit Training is also used as a rainy day fitness activity! Signs are set up in the classroom, auditorium, cafeteria, or multi-purpose room.

Sample Beginning Activity: Circuit Training

1. Students feel their pulse before starting activity.
2. Blow whistle once to start activity.
3. After seven seconds of activity, blow whistle twice; students stop activity and rotate to the next station.
4. After 15 seconds, blow whistle one time and students begin activity at the new station.
5. Continue this format until each student has exercised once at each station. Feel the pulse after every two stations.
6. Feel pulse at the end of the activity.

Suggested Stations

| STRADDLE JUMP | JOG IN PLACE WITH HIGH KNEES | GALLOP AROUND CONES | SKIP AROUND CONES |

| JUMP AND KICK | JOG IN PLACE AND CLAP | HALF-JUMPING JACKS | SLIDE AROUND CONES |

| HOP AROUND CONES | ROCK AND ROLL | JUMP AND TWIST | STUDENT CHOICE! |

Signs for circuit training are not numbered; this allows the teacher the flexibility to change the order of the activities in the circuit. Additionally, students may become confused if they begin at a station other than number one. Simplify the movements at the stations for students in kindergarten through third grade (see variations).

Variations

Additional Stations.

BENCH STEP-UPS

ZIG ZAG IN AND OUT OF CONES

AGILITY RUN WITH BEAN BAGS OR POPSICLE STICKS

SOCCER OR BASKETBALL DRIBBLING AROUND CONES

Fitness challenges. Includes three levels of difficulty, determined by the number of repetitions for the specified movement, on each circuit training sign. Each student chooses the number of repetitions appropriate for his fitness level.

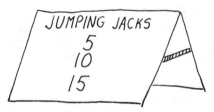

Jogging around the circuit. Add jogging to the activity as fitness levels increase. When the whistle is blown twice, instead of rotating directly to the next station, the students begin jogging around the outside of the boundaries created by the circuit signs. Students quickly advance to their next station when the whistle is blown three times. Use one specific song to designate jogging. When a previously designated song begins to play, students start jogging around the boundaries; they quickly advance to their next station when this song stops.

Animal Movements. Use the following animal movements in a circuit training activity for students in kindergarten through third grade.

FLY LIKE A BIRD

JUMP LIKE A KANGAROO

RUN LIKE A CHEETAH

SWIM LIKE A FISH

10. JOGGING

Description
Children jog at a medium pace for increasing periods of time. Jogging is an individual activity; each student moves continuously at a pace that enables her to elevate her heart rate to the target heart rate range.

Organization
Jogging, like power walking, can be organized in two ways. Students may either jog randomly within large boundaries, or run laps around boundaries marked by cones. Encourage students to jog on their own without comparing their pace (speed) with others. Comparisons will be minimized if students jog for a specific amount of time rather than for a specific distance. The advantage of jogging for time, versus jogging for distance, is everyone will finish at the same time. Emphasize self-improvement; jogging is not a competitive activity.

Jogging is a fitness activity that is not only incorporated into the physical education program, but can be carried over into recess and lunch. Many schools have implemented voluntary jogging programs in which students jog outside of the physical education class and keep a log of the time completed throughout the year.

√   Proper jogging form is stressed to prevent injuries from occurring due to improper technique. Proper jogging form includes:

1.   Look straight ahead.
2.   Hold the head still.
3.   Relax the shoulders, arms, and hands.
4.   Bend the elbows to about a 90% angle.
5.   Avoid swinging the arms across the body.
6.   Lean slightly forward.
7.   Land on the heels and roll to the toes.

Discuss and practice the concept of pacing. Initiate a discussion about pacing by asking students this question: "Should you run a mile at the same pace (speed) that you run a 50-yard dash?" The answer, of course, is no! A mile is over 35 times farther than a 50-yard dash. Ask the class to run at a pace that is best for covering a mile; then try a fifty-yard dash pace.

Sample Beginning Activity: Jogging
Encourage students to jog as long as possible; however, they are allowed to walk (fast!) when necessary.

1.   Students feel their pulse before starting activity.
2.   Jog and walk for two minutes. Use a whistle to signal changes in the method of locomotion. One whistle blast signals walking, two whistle blasts signal jogging.
3.   Alternate between jogging and walking every 10 to 20 seconds.
4.   Stop, feel pulse and discuss concepts during rest periods.

√   The feet strike the ground with a heel-to-toe motion; injuries may occur if one continuously lands on the balls of the feet.

1   **2**   **3**

Variations

Jogging with Equipment. Jog while bouncing a ball, rolling a hoop, tossing a beanbag, or dribbling a soccer ball.

Partner Jogging. Partners stand on opposite sides of a jogging track. Partner number one jogs around half of the track and tags partner number two. Partner number one cuts across the center of the track as partner number two completes the lap. Partner number two tags partner number one and cuts across the center of the track as partner one starts the second lap.

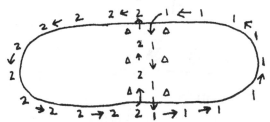

11. CONTINUITY DRILLS

Description
Rope jumping is interspersed with a variety of activities.

Organization
Students are scattered inside the boundaries; each student has his own jump rope. Students begin to jump rope on a signal from the teacher. After jumping for a specified amount of time, the teacher drops her rope and calls out a movement such as jumping jacks. Students perform jumping jacks until directed to jump rope once again. Students then pick up their ropes and jump until a new directive, such as straddle jump, is given. Activity continues with rope jumping. Give student volunteers responsibility for leading.

Playing music in the background may motivate students. If students do not know how to jump rope, they jump over a jump rope laid out in a straight line on the ground, or hold both handles in one hand and turn the rope at the side of the body while jumping. Additionally, movements such as marching in place with high knees and jogging may be used to replace rope jumping as the core activity.

This activity is vigorous and is not introduced at the beginning of the school year. It is introduced after the students have experienced Jump Rope Fitness; however, the two activities are not taught consecutively.

Sample Beginning Activity: Continuity Drills
1. Students feel their pulse before starting activity.
2. Jump rope for seven seconds.
3. Drop the rope and straddle jump for seven seconds.

4. Jump rope for seven seconds.
5. Drop the rope and jog in place and clap for seven seconds.
6. Stop and feel pulse.
7. Jump rope for seven seconds.
8. Drop the rope and jump and twist for seven seconds. Hands in the air!

9. Jump rope for seven seconds.
10. Drop the rope and march in place with high knees for seven seconds. Slap your knees!
11. Stop and feel pulse.
12. Jump rope for seven seconds.
13. Repeat previous activities or add new ones.

Variation

Change the rope jumping pattern. Additional patterns include:
1. Fast time: one jump per turn of the rope
2. Slow time: two jumps per turn of the rope
3. Side to side

12. NEW LEADER

Description
Students move in pairs. One student leads, the other follows. Students then alternate roles. Movements selected are non-stop and vigorous enough to elevate the pulse to the target heart rate range for several minutes.

Organization
Students exercise in pairs (scattered) within boundaries that are large enough to permit students to move freely without bumping into each other. One student starts out as the leader, the other is the follower. The leader begins exercising and the follower imitates the movements. After 15 to 20 seconds, the teacher blows the whistle one time and the follower becomes the new leader. When the whistle is blown again (one time), the original leader resumes that role. This procedure is repeated several times. On two whistles from the teacher, the pairs break up and each student finds a new partner. Play music in a central area so all students can hear it!

Sample Beginning Activity: New Leader
This activity contains examples of exercises the students may perform when serving as the leader. Give the students a list of acceptable cardiovascular fitness activities. Discourage exercises such as modified sit-ups and push-ups during this activity; most often these exercises do not adequately elevate the heart rate.

1. Students feel their pulse before starting activity.
2. Jog in place and clap for 10 seconds. Lift the knees high!
3. Jumping Jacks for 10 seconds.
4. Skip for 10 seconds. Swing your arms!

5. On one whistle blast, the follower becomes the new leader.

6. Feel pulse before resuming activity.
7. Jump and clap for 10 seconds. Jump high!
8. Leap within the boundaries for 10 seconds. Change the lead leg!
9. Jump and kick for 10 seconds.
10. On two whistle blasts, find a new partner and feel pulse before resuming activity.
11. Students continue to lead each other in cardiovascular fitness activities. The whistle is blown every 15 to 20 seconds. If fitness levels are low, the students walk and feel their pulse each time the whistle is blown. A beginning activity may last two to three minutes.

Variation

Groups of Four. Begin in groups of two. After both students have had the opportunity to lead, the whistle is blown four times. Each pair of students finds another pair, and they begin to exercise in groups of four.

Line Up. On the whistle signal, the leader (first person in the line) moves to the back of the line and the second person in line becomes the new leader.

13. CHALLENGE COURSES

Description

Students move continuously through a group of stations or challenges; a specified number of repetitions of each exercise is performed at each station. Each student exercises at his own pace as he moves through the course.

Organization

Position ten to fifteen stations or challenges 10 to 20 feet apart to form a large oval. Place signs designating each station on the ground or against a cone; each sign includes the name of the exercise (or challenge), an illustration of the exercise, and the number of repetitions to be performed before moving to the next station. Assign two or three students to start at each station. Before activity begins, explain each activity and the direction of rotation. Signal students to begin; encourage them to move through the course at their own pace.

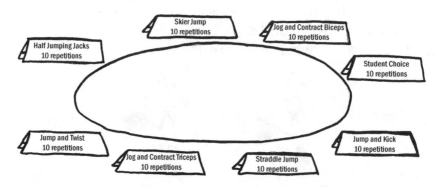

Sample Beginning Activity: Challenge Courses

1. Students feel their pulse before starting activity.
2. On a signal (one whistle blast or music), the students begin exercising at their own pace for 10 to 15 seconds.
3. Stop and feel pulse on signal (two whistle blasts or silence).
4. On signal (one whistle blast or music), the students resume activity.
5. Continue the above format for a total of two to three minutes. Allow the students to stop and feel their pulse after every 10 to 15 seconds of activity.

Suggested Stations: start with five repetitions of each exercise

JUMP AND TWIST

JOG AND CONTRACT BICEPS

JOG AND CONTRACT TRICEPS

STRADDLE JUMP

HALF JUMPING JACKS

JUMP AND KICK

STUDENT CHOICE!

?

JOG IN PLACE WITH HIGH KNEES

JUMP BACK AND FORTH OVER A ROPE OR AN IMAGINARY LINE ON THE GROUND

Variations

Figure-Eight Movements. Place four cones, chalk marks, or beanbags on the ground for each exercise station. A different locomotor movement is used for each trip around the figure-eight pattern. Set up one Figure-Eight course for each group of three to four students to avoid crowding.

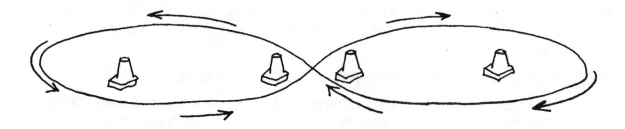

Zig Zag Course. Position five to ten cones, chalk marks, or beanbags in a straight line, 10 to 20 feet apart. The students perform various locomotor movements while "zigging" and "zagging" in and out of the cones. When the student reaches the last cone, he jogs back to the beginning of the course and prepares to move through it again. Set up one course for each group of three to four students to avoid crowding.

Allow the students to choose the locomotor movements. Each student performs the locomotor movement of her choice as long as she moves continuously!

14. SQUAD LEADER EXERCISES

Description

One student leads three or four other students in cardiovascular fitness activities. This is an advanced activity that is introduced after students have participated regularly in fitness activities for two to three months.

Organization

Squad Leader Exercises is an excellent activity for developing leadership and independence in students; responsibility for leading is given to the students.

Each squad leader takes her squad (three to four students) to a designated area and leads them in activity. The squad leader is informed of his role a few days ahead of time and given an activity that may be practiced at home. This activity must be continuous to improve cardiovascular fitness; the students move from one exercise to the next without stopping. All students are given the opportunity to serve as leader; however, students are allowed to decline. Music is played in a central area so all students hear it.

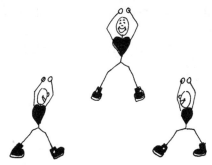

Sample Beginning Activity: Squad Leader Exercises

1. Students feel their pulse before starting activity.
2. Jog in place for 10 counts.
3. March and clap for 10 counts. Knees high!
4. Jump and twist for 10 counts.
5. Half jumping jacks for 10 counts.
6. Walk and feel pulse.
7. Follow the leader. The squad follows the leader around the activity area while the leader performs the following movements: jogging, hopping, skipping, galloping, sliding, and leaping.
8. Feel pulse at the conclusion of the activity.

Variations

Student Activities. Allow the squad leaders to create their own activity. Specify exercises to be included and the amount of time the activity is to last.

Add Equipment. Dribble basketballs or soccer balls, jump rope, or keep beach balls or balloons up in the air while moving.

---

15. PACER (Progressive Aerobic Cardiovascular Endurance Run)

Description

PACER stands for Progressive Aerobic Cardiovascular Endurance Run. The student runs as long as possible back and forth across a 20-meter distance at a specific pace. The pace during the first minute is the slowest pace; the pace increases slightly as each minute passes. The total number of laps completed is the final score.

Organization

Mark two lines 20 meters apart with cones, tape, or chalk. Students select a partner; one partner lines up behind the start line to run while the other counts laps. Once all students are lined up at the start line, the cadence tape begins. Students run across the 20-meter distance and touch the line with one foot by the time the beep sounds. At the sound of the beep students run back to the other line. Once all students in the first group are finished, the lap counters become the runners.

Sample Beginning PACER

The following beginning activity is a modified PACER designed to provide students with the experience of running back and forth between two lines at a designated pace; the lines are five meters apart and the pace is the same as the pace for the 20-meter distance on the *FITNESSGRAM/ACTIVITYGRAM* CD.

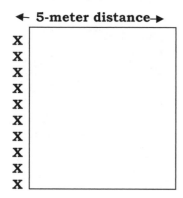

1. Students feel their pulse before activity.
2. Students run across the five-meter distance and touch the line with one foot.
3. At the sound of the beep, students turn around and run back. Students wait for the beep before running the other direction.
4. Triple beeps alert the runners that the pace is increasing.
5. Students stop when they fail to reach the line before the beep for the second time. After the first incomplete lap, they are given the chance to catch back up.
6. When students can no longer continue, they begin to walk and stretch in cool-down area.

Variations

Increase the distance between the lines. The distance between lines is increased gradually. The goal is for students to have fun and to be active as long as possible. Ultimately, when the PACER is used as an assessment item, the lines are 20 meters apart as designated in the *FITNESSGRAM/ACTIVITYGRAM* manual.

Summary

Cardiovascular fitness may be the most important component of health-related physical fitness. This chapter provides concepts that will help students to understand what cardiovascular fitness is and why it is important to lifetime health. The activities are designed to be enjoyable, non-competitive, and to develop each student's feelings of competence and confidence.

References

Cooper Institute for Aerobics Research. (2005). *FITNESSGRAM/ACTIVITYGRAM test administration manual.* Champaign, IL: Human Kinetics.

Corbin, C. B., Lindsey, R., & Welk, G.J. (2002). *Concepts of physical fitness* (10th ed.). St. Louis: McGraw-Hill.

Corbin, C. B., & Lindsey, R. (2003). *Fitness for life* (5th ed.). Glenview, IL: Scott, Foresman and Company.

Mohnsen, B. (1994). *Concepts of physical education.* Reston, VA: NASPE.

Pangrazi, R. (2007). *Dynamic physical education for elementary school children* (15th ed.). San Francisco, CA: Pearson Education Corporation.

Tudor-Locke, C. (2002). Taking steps towards increased physical activity: Using pedometers to measure and motivate. *President's Council on Physical Fitness and Sports Research Digest, 3*(17).

Tudor-Locke, C., & Myers, A.M. ((2001). Methodological considerations for researchers and practitioners using pedometers to measure physical (ambulatory) activity. *Research Quarterly for Exercise and Sport, 72*(1), 1-12.

U.S. Department of Health and Human Services. (1996). *Physical activity and health: A report of the surgeon general.* Atlanta, GA: U.S. Department of Health and Human Services, Centers for Disease Control and Prevention, National Center for Chronic Disease Prevention and Health Promotion.

Websites

American Heart Association   www.americanheart.org
Cardiovascular System Teacher's Guide
   http://www.KidsHealth.org/classroom/9to12/body/systems/cardiovascular.pdf

The Reproducible Handout for the Cardiovascular System
   http://www.KidsHealth.org/classroom/9to12/body/systems/cardiovascular_handout.pdf

Chapter 12
Body Composition

Obesity is a global health problem affecting both children and adults (See Chapter 3 for more details on the childhood obesity/type 2 diabetes epidemic). Childhood is the most appropriate time to promote physically active lifestyles and wise nutritional choices that will minimize the development of obesity. Quality physical education experiences that include maximal physical activity and education focused on the interrelationship between body composition, physical activity and nutritional choices will empower children to make healthy lifestyle choices.

This chapter contains concepts related to body composition and physical activity. Additionally, because of the effect of one's food choices on body composition, concepts related to nutrition are also included. Activities for developing and maintaining healthy levels of body composition are the same as the activities for improving cardiovascular fitness; thus, activities are not included in this chapter. Refer to Chapter 11 for activities to achieve or maintain healthy levels of body composition.

BODY COMPOSITION AND PHYSICAL ACTIVITY CONCEPTS

The following concepts apply to body composition and nutrition. Integrating these concepts into physical education lessons provides students with the understandings necessary to assess, achieve and maintain healthy levels of body composition. Chapter 3 provides in-depth information on body composition; please review this chapter prior to reading through the concepts. It may be helpful to read through all of the concepts before selecting one or two to discuss in each lesson. The concepts are divided into the following two sections:

♥ The "What's-Why's-How's" of Body Composition
♥ The "What's-Why's-How's" of Nutrition

The "What's" of Body Composition

1. **What is body composition?** Body composition is the amount of fat, muscle, bone, and other vital parts of the body. It is also referred to as relative leanness. In children, the two most common methods for assessing body composition are Body Mass Index (BMI) and skinfold measurements.

2. ***What is Body Mass Index (BMI)?*** BMI is one way to measure body composition. BMI is a number calculated from a person's weight and height. There are two formulas to measure BMI, one uses kilograms and meters and the other uses pounds and feet to measure weight and height. The formulas and examples for calculating BMI are presented in Chapter 3 (Figure 3.4) Students in grades three and above can calculate their own BMI.

3. **What is the limitation of using a scale to determine body composition?** Muscle weighs more than fat. Thus, it is recommended that very muscular children or adults who's BMI puts them in the "at risk for overweight" or "overweight category," also be administered skinfold measurements to get a more accurate estimate of body composition (see skinfold explanation below).

4. ***What are skinfold measurements?*** Skinfold measurements are a second method for measuring the amount of fat in the body. A skinfold is two thicknesses of skin and the amount of fat that lies between them. Half of a person's fat is located just beneath the skin. Skinfold calipers are used to measure skinfolds (in millimeters). Skinfold measurements provide a more accurate estimate of body fat because the actual fat is measured without concern for a person's weight. However, to insure accuracy of skinfold measurements, training in the use of skinfold calipers is required. BMI is the recommended assessment for use by people not trained in skinfold assessment.

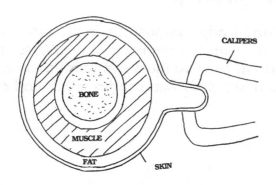

5. ***What is a healthy level of body composition for youth?*** The
   FITNESSGRAM Manual (Cooper Institute for Aerobic Research, 2005)
   contains Healthy Fitness Zones (HFZ) for youth aged five to 17 based on
   both BMI and skinfolds. For example, in *FITNESSGRAM*, the BMI HFZ
   range for an 11-year-old boy is 14.3 to 21; the HFZ percent body fat,
   determined by taking skinfold measurements, for an 11-year-old boy is
   below 25% fat.

6. ***What are the differences between healthy levels of body
   composition for children and those for adults?***   There is little
   difference between healthy levels of body composition for children and
   those for adults. Obesity is a health problem for people of all ages;
   however, childhood is the most appropriate time to address problems or
   potential problems and attempt to make the necessary behavior change
   to remedy problems.

7. ***What are the benefits of a healthy level of body composition?*** A
   healthy level of body composition will minimize one's risk of high
   cholesterol, high blood pressure, type 2 diabetes, coronary heart disease
   and some cancers. Additionally, healthy levels of body composition
   minimize one's risk of emotional and social problems related to excess
   body fat.

8. ***What happens to body composition when one participates regularly
   in physical activity?*** People who participate regularly in physical
   activity usually have less fat than people who are not physically active on
   a regular basis.

9. ***What are some activities that can help one to achieve and
   maintain healthy levels of body composition?*** Activities that one can
   use to achieve and maintain healthy levels of body composition are the
   same as those that develop cardiovascular fitness. The following
   cardiovascular fitness activities can be performed outside of school:
   walking, jogging, ice, in-line and roller skating, skate boarding, cycling,
   hiking, swimming, dancing, cross-country skiing, and rowing.
   Additionally, activities such as raking leaves for 30 minutes, gardening
   for 30 to 45 minutes, and washing and waxing a car for 45 to 60 minutes
   (see Chapter 4) burn substantial calories.

10. ***What is the truth about spot reducing?*** Some people believe fat can be reduced or even eliminated in certain areas of the body by performing special exercises. The concept of spot reducing, however, is a myth. When fat is lost, it is lost from all areas of the body not just from one specific "spot." Fat is used for energy from all cells of the body during moderate to vigorous, non-stop cardiovascular fitness activities.

11. ***What are the FITT Guidelines for body composition?***
    F = Frequency. Perform moderate to vigorous physical activity (MVPA) four to seven days per week.

    I = Intensity. Participate in MVPA. Exercising within the Target Heart Rate Range (see Chapter 11) is desirable but not necessary.

    T = Time. Participate in MVPA for 30 to 60 minutes daily. The greater one's time in activity, the greater the caloric expenditure.

    T = Type. Perform both intermittent and continuous MVPA to reduce body fat and maintain a healthy level of body composition. Ultimately, participation in any type of physical activity will burn calories and positively affect body composition.

12. **What is the largest organ of the body?** The skin is the largest organ of the body; the skin of the average adult weighs about 12 pounds.

The "Why's" of Body Composition

1. ***Why is too much fat (obesity) a health risk?*** For every extra pound of fat a person carries, the heart must pump blood through an extra mile of blood vessels. Children and adults with high levels of fat have increased risk of type 2 diabetes, high cholesterol, high blood pressure and some cancers. Excess fat may also negatively affect one's emotional health.

2. ***Why are children and adults with high levels of fat at higher risk of type 2 diabetes?*** High levels of fat may reduce the ability of insulin to facilitate the absorption of glucose into the cells. When glucose is not absorbed into the cells, it remains in the bloodstream and is then excreted in the urine. People with type 2 diabetes who have high levels of fat, can usually reduce the severity of or totally eliminate the diabetes through fat reduction achieved through increased physical activity and decreased caloric consumption.

3. ***Why is excessive thinness a health risk?*** Dangerously low levels of body fat may cause growth to be stunted, puberty to be delayed, and other serious health problems, including death! Three conditions that may lead to dangerously low levels of body fat are: Anorexia Nervosa, Bulimia, and "Fear of Obesity."

♥ **Anorexia Nervosa** is characterized by a failure to eat, regurgitation when food is ingested, and compulsive exercise.

♥ **Bulimia** is characterized by erratic eating habits, and regurgitation to prevent the digestion of foods eaten.

♥ **"Fear of Obesity"** is characterized by excessive concern for leanness that may eventually lead to Anorexia Nervosa or Bulimia.

4. *Why is it important for children to maintain healthy levels of body composition?* It is important to maintain healthy levels of body composition during the childhood years. The belief that baby fat disappears with age is a myth; once a child becomes fat, he has a high risk of becoming a fat adult. Seven out of 10 obese youth will grow into obese adults.

The "How's" of Body Composition

1. *How does excess body fat affect one's performance on physical fitness assessments?* Excess body fat may result in decreased performance on cardiovascular fitness (PACER and one-mile run) and muscular strength and endurance (push-ups, curl-ups) tests. Improvements in body composition will generally result in improved performance on these assessments.

2. *How do the principles of exercise apply to body composition?*
♥ **Overload.** Increase the frequency, or time of activity to achieve healthy levels of body composition. MVPA is recommended, but not required) to reduce body fat and maintain a healthy level of body composition.
♥ **Progression.** Gradually increase the amount of time or frequency of participation in MVPA. The longer and more often one is active, the more fat she will use for energy.
♥ **Specificity.** Perform MVPA.
♥ **Regularity.** Perform MVPA four to seven days per week. It is recommended that no more than two days elapse between workouts.
♥ **Individual Differences.** Encourage each child to exercise at her own pace and to achieve a level of body composition within the Healthy Fitness Zone. Avoid comparing students' levels body composition; each person is unique due to differences in body fat, nutrition, health, motivation, and genetic make-up.

NUTRITION CONCEPTS

The "What's" of Nutrition

1. *What nutrients are necessary for a healthy life?* Several nutrients are necessary for one to live a healthy life. These nutrients include: proteins, carbohydrates, fats, fiber, minerals, vitamins, and water.

♥ **Protein** helps to build bones, skin, muscle fibers, and many other tissues in the body. Proteins are found in meat, fish, poultry, eggs, milk, peas, beans, and nuts.

♥ **Carbohydrates** provide energy. There are two types of carbohydrates: simple and complex. "Simple" carbohydrates are found in candy, cakes and many pastry products. Simple carbohydrates are not nutritious;

aside from containing sugar, which provides energy, they have no other nutritional value. On the other hand, "Complex" carbohydrates, found in vegetables, spaghetti, whole wheat bread and beans are a healthy source of energy.

♥ **Fat** provides energy, keeps the body warm, and protects the body from injury. There are four kinds of fat, monounsaturated, polyunsaturated, saturated and trans fat.

♥ **Monounsaturated Fat.** Monounsaturated fat is healthy fat; it may lower one's risk of heart disease and other health problems. Monounsaturated fat is found in avocados, nuts, seeds, and anything made with olive oil, peanut oil, or canola oil.

♥ **Polyunsaturated Fat.** Polyunsaturated fat is healthy fat. There are two types of polyunsaturated fat: omega-3 fatty acid and omega-6 fatty acid. Both may positively effect depression and blood pressure.

♥ **Saturated Fat.** Saturated fat is unhealthy fat. Foods containing saturated fat (red meat, butter, whole milk, ice cream, anything made with palm oil or coconut oil) may raise the cholesterol levels in the blood. The body needs some cholesterol; however, if the body gets too much cholesterol, it will clog up the blood vessels and make it difficult for the blood to move through them.

♥ **Trans Fat.** Trans fat is unhealthy fat. The fat in processed, packaged and fried foods often goes through a process called hydrogenation; trans fat is a by-product of this process. The word "hydrogenated" usually appears on the nutrition facts label of a food containing trans-fat. Trans fat is found in margarine, fried foods and packaged doughnuts, crackers and cookies. Studies have connected trans fat with breast cancer, colon cancer and type 2 diabetes.

♥ **Fiber.** Eating a diet high in dietary fiber promotes healthy bowel function. Additionally, a diet rich in fruits, vegetables and whole grain products that contain dietary fiber, and are low in saturated fat and cholesterol, may reduce heart disease risk.

♥ **Minerals** are metallic elements that are vital for proper cell functioning. Many minerals are found in the muscles, teeth, and bones. Calcium and phosphorus are the two most abundant minerals in the body. The calcium and phosphorus in the teeth and bones account for 58% to 85% of the total percentage of minerals in the body. Sodium is another example of a mineral.

> ♥ Experts recommend 1,000mg of calcium daily for adults on a 2000 calorie diet; however, for adolescent girls and post-menopausal women, they recommend 1,300mg and 1,200mg respectively.

> ♥ Too much sodium may cause high blood pressure; experts recommend a daily maximum of 2,400mg.

♥ **Vitamins** are substances needed by the body in very small amounts to perform specific functions within the cells. Our bodies need vitamins to be healthy. Food contains vitamins. Healthy people who eat well-balanced meals probably get enough vitamins without taking supplements. It has been estimated that Americans spend between $300 million and $500 million annually on unnecessary vitamin supplements.

♥ **Water.** The body needs water even more than it needs food. Water is the main ingredient in the body.

2. ***What is the United States Department of Agriculture's MyPyramid.gov?*** MyPyramid.gov (Figure 12.1), symbolizes a personal approach to healthy eating and physical activity.

Figure 12.1   MyPyramid.gov - Steps to a Healthier You

The steps on the left, the six sections within the pyramid and their differing widths, the wide base and narrow point at the top of each section, the slogan, and the URL each have meaning in understanding and applying the pyramid.

- **Physical activity**, on a daily basis, is represented by a person climbing steps on the side of the pyramid.
- **Variety,** and the importance of consuming food from all groups daily, is symbolized by the six color bands representing the five food groups and oils.
- **Proportionality** is emphasized by the differing widths of the food group bands. The widths represent a general recommendation for the proportion of food to eat from each group on a daily basis.
- **Moderation** is represented by the narrowing of each food group from bottom to top. The wide base of each stripe represents wholesome, healthier foods, with little or no solid fats, added sugar or calorie sweeteners. The narrow top represents the higher-calorie foods in each food group.
- **Gradual improvement** is encouraged by the slogan "STEPS TO A HEALTHIER YOU."
- **Personalization** is represented by the URL at which each person, based upon individual data, can determine the kinds and amounts of food to each day.

The pyramid utilizes a color scheme to represent the five food groups and oils. To decipher the pyramid depicted in a half-tone format, shown in Figure 12.1, the colors, from left to right (after the steps) are orange, green, red, yellow, blue, and purple, representing the corresponding groups of grains, vegetables, fruits, oils, milk, and meat and beans.

Grains (orange)	Vegetables (green)	Fruits (red)	O i l s	Milk (blue)	Meat and Beans (purple)

3. *What is the USDA recommendation for each group?* *The USDA recommends the following for each of the six groups.*

- **Grains (orange).** Consume five to eight ounces of grain daily; at least three ounces are to consist of whole grain breads, crackers, pasta, cereals or rice.
- **Vegetables (green).** Consume two and one-half cups of vegetables per day. Select from all five vegetable subgroups (dark green, orange, legumes, starchy vegetables, and other vegetables several times a week.
- **Fruits (red).** Consume two cups of fruit daily.
- **Oils (yellow).** Emphasize fat sources from fish, nuts and vegetable oils, and limit solid fats like butter, stick margarine, lard and shortening.
- **Milk (blue).** Consume three cups per day of fat-free or low-fat milk or equivalent milk products daily.
- **Beans and Meats (purple).** Choose lean meats and poultry, varying protein choices with more fish, beans peas, nuts and seeds. One can visit the interactive website at www.MyPyramid.gov to learn more about the pyramid and develop a "personalized" eating plan.

4. ***What are the dietary guidelines of the Departments of Health and Human Services and Agriculture?***

♥ **Calories.** Balance calories between the amount of calories consumed and the amount of calories expended for energy. For moderately active people between 31 and 50, general recommendations for caloric consumption are 2,000 per day for women and 2,400 to 2,600 for men. More specific recommendations for caloric consumption are determined by gender, body type and level of activity.

♥ **Physical Activity.** The IOM (see chapter 4) physical activity guideline include the following two recommendations concerning body composition:
  ♥ Participate regularly in 60 minutes to maintain weight and prevent weight gain
  ♥ Participate regularly in 60 to 90 minutes per day to sustain weight loss

♥ **Nutrition.** Eat foods high in nutrients and fiber and low in saturated and trans fat, cholesterol, added sugars and salt.

♥ **Fruits and Vegetables.** Eat at least 4½ cups of fruits and vegetables per day for a 2,000 calorie per day diet. Modify consumption based upon daily caloric intake.

♥ **Carbohydrates.** Eat fiber-rich whole fruits and vegetables and whole grains often. Eat and drink little added sugar or caloric sweeteners.

♥ **Fat.** Consume as little trans fat as possible. Consume 20-35 percent of daily calories from fat, primarily monounsaturated or polyunsaturated. Limit calories from saturated fat to less than 10 percent of daily total. Healthy individuals consume no more than 300 milligrams of cholesterol per day; those at high risk for heart disease consume no more than 200 milligrams.

♥ **Salt.** Limit salt to approximately one level teaspoon per day.

5. ***What is a nutrition facts label?*** Nutrition labels provide information for use in making food choices. Most packaged foods in the grocery store list nutrition information on the package in a section called the "Nutrition Facts." Foods that are exempt from the label include foods in very small packages, foods prepared in the store, and foods made by small manufacturers. Figure 12.2 depicts an example of a Nutrition Facts label for a bag of potato chips. A step by step explanation of the label follows.

Figure 12.2 A nutrition facts food label for a 9 ounce bag of potato chips

Nutrition Facts
Serving Size 1 oz. (28g/About 14 chips)
Servings Per Container 9

Amount per serving	
Calories 150	Calories from Fat 90

	% daily value*
Total Fat 10g	**15%**
Saturated Fat 1g	**5%**
Polyunsaturated Fat 3g	
Monosaturated Fat 6g	
Trans Fat 0g	
Cholesterol 0mg	**0%**
Sodium 180mg	**7%**
Total Carbohydrate 15g	**5%**
Dietary Fiber 1g	**4%**
Sugars 0g	
Protein 2g	

Vitamin A 0% *	Vitamin C 10%
Calcium 0% *	Iron 2%
Vitamin E 10%	Thiamine 2%
Niacin 6%	Vitamin B6 4%
Phosphorus 4%	Magnesium 4%

*Percent Daily Values are based on a 2,000 calorie diet. Your daily values may be higher or lower depending on your calorie needs:

	Calories	2,000	2,500
Total Fat	Less than	65g	80g
Sat Fat	Less than	20g	25g
Cholesterol	Less than	300mg	300mg
Sodium	Less than	2,400mg	2,400mg
Total Carbohydrate		300g	375g
Dietary Fiber		5g	30g

Calories per gram:
Fat 9   Carbohydrate 4   Protein 4

Ingredients: Potatoes, Sunflower Oil and Sa

♥ **Serving Size.** Start at the top with the serving size and the number of servings per package (see Figure 12.3). Serving sizes are standardized to make it easier to compare similar foods; they are provided in units such as ounces, cups or pieces, followed by the metric amount (number of grams). The information listed on the label is for one serving size, not for the entire package. The serving size listed on the food label may not be the same as the serving a person normally eats. If one consumes twice the serving listed on the label, the numbers for the nutrients listed (calories, total fat, cholesterol, sodium, total carbohydrate, protein) are doubled. In the sample label, one serving of potato chips equals about 14 chips, if a person eats 28 chips, he consumes two serving sizes. Thus, the calories and other nutrient numbers, including the % daily values as shown on the sample label are multiplied by two.

Figure 12.3 Serving size and servings per bag of potato chips

Serving Size 1oz 14 chips (28g))
Servings Per Container 9

♥ **Calories and Calories from Fat.** Calories provide a measure of the energy provided from one serving. The number of servings consumed determines the number of calories eaten. In the sample label, there are 150 calories in one serving of potato chips (see Figure 12.4). Consuming two serving sizes equates to 300 calories: 180 (2 X 90) of the 300 calories consumed are from fat.

Figure 12.4 Calories and calories from fat in one serving size of chips

Amount Per Serving	
Calories 150	Calories from Fat 90

♥ **Nutrient content and percent of daily value (%DV).** The nutrient section shows some key nutrients that impact health. The Percent Daily Value (%DV) on the right provides the percent of the recommended daily requirement, based on a 2,000 calorie diet, contained in one serving. If a person needs more or fewer calories, the daily values would be different. A product is a good source of a particular nutrient if one serving provides 10 to 19% of the DV, high in a given nutrient if it contains 20% or more of the DV, and low in that nutrient if the DV is 5% or less. One can use the nutrition facts label to both limit undesirable nutrients and increase necessary nutrients.

♥The nutrients in Figure 12.5 are those generally consumed in adequate amounts, sometimes even too much. Eating too much fat, saturated fat, trans fat, cholesterol, or sodium may increase risk of certain diseases.

Figure 12.5 Nutrients to watch in one serving size of potato chips

NUTRIENTS	%DV
Total Fat 10g	15%
Saturated Fat 1g	2%
Polyunsaturated 3g	
Monosaturated 6g	
Trans Fat 0g	0%
Cholesterol 0g	0%
Sodium 180mg	7%

Most people do not consume enough dietary fiber, vitamins A and C, calcium and iron. Eating enough of these nutrients promotes good health. For example, eating a healthy amount of dietary fiber promotes healthy bowel function, and consuming recommended amounts of calcium may reduce risk of osteoporosis. Information on the following additional nutrients are also included on the sample label: Vitamin E, Thiamin, Niacin, Vitamin B6, Phosphorus and Magnesium (see Figure 12.6). An asterisk (*) signifies that one serving contains less than 2% of the DV% of the nutrient.

Figure 12. 6 Nutrients and %DV in one serving size of potato chips

NUTRIENTS	%DV
Dietary Fiber 1g	4%
Vitamin A *	0%
Vitamin C	10%
Calcium *	0%
Iron	2%
Vitamin E	10%
Thiamine	2%
Niacin	6%
Vitamin B6	4%
Phosphorus	4%
Magnesium	4%

2. **What determines a "single serving size"?** The serving size is listed at the top of the Nutrition Facts; however, some foods do not have a label. The following are helpful tips to determine one serving size of several different foods (www.eatright.org).

♥ **Meat, poultry and fish** – 2 to 3 ounces –deck of cards or size of the fist
♥ **Cheese** – 1½ ounces – a domino, C battery or your thumb
♥ **Burrito** – bar of soap
♥ **Fruit** – ½ cup – baseball, or small computer mouse
♥ **Cooked vegetables** – ½ cup – small computer mouse
♥ **Potato** – 60 watt light bulb
♥ **Butter** – 1 die
♥ **Pasta and rice** – ½ cup – the size of the fist

3. *What is the difference in calories in one gram of protein, carbohydrate, and fat?* One gram of protein and one gram of carbohydrate each have four calories. One gram of fat has nine calories, over twice as many (see bottom of Nutrition Facts label).

4. *What is the difference between the terms "calorie free" and "low calorie?"*
♥ *"Calorie free"* denotes less than 5 calories per serving.
♥ *"Low calorie"* denotes 40 calories or less.

5. ***What is the difference between the terms "fat free," "saturated fat free," "low fat," "low saturated fat" and "'reduced fat' or 'less fat?'"***

♥ *"Fat free"* denotes less than 0.5 grams (g) of fat or saturated fat per serving.

♥ *"Saturated fat free"* denotes less than 0.5 g of saturated fat or less than 5 grams of trans fat per serving.

♥ *"Low fat"* denotes 3 g or less of total fat per serving.

♥ *"Low saturated fat"* denotes 1 g or less of saturated fat per serving.

♥ *"'Reduced fat' or 'less fat"* denotes at least 25% less fat per serving than the regular version.

6. ***What is the difference between the terms "'sodium free' or 'salt free,'" "very low sodium," "low sodium," and "'reduced sodium' or 'less sodium?'"***

♥ *"'Sodium free' or 'salt free'"* denotes less than 5 milligrams (mg) of sodium per serving.

♥ *"Very low sodium"* denotes 35 mg of sodium or less per serving.

♥ *"Low sodium"* denotes 140 mg of sodium or less per serving.

♥ *"'Reduced sodium or 'less sodium"* denotes at least 25% less sodium per serving than the regular version.

7. ***What is the difference between the terms "cholesterol free," "low cholesterol" and "'reduced cholesterol' or 'less cholesterol?'"***

♥ *"Cholesterol free"* denotes less than 2 mg of cholesterol per serving.

♥ *"Low cholesterol"* denotes 20 mg of cholesterol or less per serving.

♥ *"'Reduced cholesterol' or 'less cholesterol"* denotes at least 25% less cholesterol per serving than the regular version.

8. ***What is the difference between the terms "sugar free" and "reduced sugar?"***

♥ *"Sugar free"* denotes less than 0.5 grams (g) of sugar per serving.

♥ *"'Reduced sugar"* denotes at least 25% less sugar per serving than the regular version.

9. ***What is the difference between the terms "high fiber" and "good source of fiber?"***

♥ *"High fiber"* denotes 5 grams (g) or more of fiber per serving.

♥ *"'Good source of fiber"* denotes 2.5 g to 4.9 g of fiber per serving.

The "Why" of Nutrition

1. ***Why is water important for health?*** Water is the main "ingredient" of the body! The body needs water even more than it needs food. Many doctors recommend drinking eight to sixteen cups (eight ounces) of water each day! The body is about 75% water and 25 percent solid matter.

Muscle consists of approximately 75% water. Fat consists of approximately 20% to 25% water. For two people of the same body weight, the total body water will be larger for the person with the greater muscle mass. Different parts of the body have different water content.

- ♥ The brain is 85% water.
- ♥ The heart is 75% water.
- ♥ The lungs are 86% water.
- ♥ The liver is 86% water.
- ♥ The kidneys are 83% water.
- ♥ The blood is 94% water.

The "How's" of Nutrition

1. ***How many calories are in one pound of body weight?*** One pound of body weight is roughly equivalent to 3500 calories. It does not matter whether the calories come from proteins, carbohydrates or fat. A calorie is a calorie is a calorie.

2. ***How does one acquire excess fat?*** The way a person acquires fat is to consume more calories than he expends for energy. Food contains calories; calories provide energy and are necessary for a person to live. Any calories consumed that are not expended as energy are converted to fat. There is a fine line between being in and out of energy balance.

- ♥ If, on a daily basis for one year, a person's caloric intake exceeds his caloric expenditure by 100 calories (one glass of apple juice or two tablespoons of certain salad dressings), he will gain 10 pounds per year. This is calculated by multiplying 100 (calories) X 365 (days in a year). Thus, consuming 36,500 extra calories in one year results in a 10 pound weight gain (36500 extra calories/3500 calories in one pound =10.4 lbs.)

- ♥ Similarly, if a person becomes more sedentary (taking the escalator instead of the stairs) and thus, his caloric expenditure decreases by 100 calories daily for one year (while keeping caloric intake the same), he will gain 10 pounds per year.

3. ***How many calories do various activities burn?*** Activities burn calories based upon the time and the intensity of the activity. Some examples, provided by the American Dietetic Association (www.eatright.org) of activities, when performed at a moderate level, that burn 100 calories follow:

- Roller skating, jogging or aerobic dance for 15 minutes
- Gardening, washing the car, walking the dog and pushing a stroller for 20 minutes
- Walking one mile
- Bicycling for 25 minutes

4. ***How does someone lose fat?*** A combination of increased physical activity and decreased caloric consumption (especially high-fat, high-calorie, low-nutrition foods) is recommended to lose fat.

- The maximum recommended weight loss is no more than one to two pounds per week.
- There are 3,500 calories in a pound of body weight. To lose one pound of per week, five hundred calories per day must be eliminated from one's normal daily caloric intake or burned through physical activity. Five hundred calories per day, equals 3,500 calories per week or one pound (Figure 12.7).

Figure 12.7   Formula For Losing One Pound of Fat Per Week

$$\underset{\substack{\text{calories} \\ \text{per day}}}{\textbf{500}} \quad \textbf{X} \quad \underset{\substack{\text{days} \\ \text{per week}}}{\textbf{7}} \quad \textbf{=} \quad \underset{\substack{\text{pound per week}}}{\textbf{1}}$$

- If fat is lost slowly, it is more likely to stay off than if it is lost quickly.
- Crash dieting or skipping meals may result in weakness or sickness It is recommended that no less than 900 calories be consumed each day.
- Fasting for extended periods of time may result in a slower metabolism.
- A person may lose fat and gain muscle at the same time by reducing caloric intake, while at the same time, increasing physical activity. Fat does not "turn" into muscle; losing fat and increasing muscle are two separate processes. Some people who lose weight still look flabby. Regular participation in physical activity and muscular strength and endurance activities will help to firm up the muscles so the body looks toned. When dieting alone is used to lose fat, the body may become flabby.

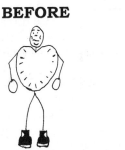   

BEFORE   **AFTER**

♥   Physical activity uses up calories. Every activity uses up calories, even sleeping! Continuous MVPA sustained for at least 30 to 90 minutes, is the best type of activity for expending calories.

Summary

Body composition is a vital component of health related physical fitness. A health related physical fitness-based physical education program that includes regular participation in physical activity and the teaching and application of body composition and nutrition concepts, will empower children to make healthy activity and food choices.

References

Batmanghelidj, F. (2003). You're not sick, you're thirsty! Water for health, for healing, for life. NY: Time Warner Book Group.

Borushek, A. (2006). The calorie king: Calorie, fat and carbohydrate counter. Costa Mesa, CA: Family Health Publications. (www.calorieking.com)

Cooper Institute for Aerobics Research. (2005). *FITNESSGRAM/ ACTIVITYGRAM test administration manual.* Champaign, IL: Human Kinetics.

Corbin, C. B., Lindsey, R., & Welk, G.J. (2002). *Concepts of physical fitness* (10th Ed.). St. Louis: McGraw-Hill.

Corbin, C.B., (2003). *Fitness for life* (5th ed.). Glenview, IL: Scott, Foresman and Company.

Epstein, L.H. Valoski, A., Wing, R.R., & McCurly, J. (1990). Ten-year follow-up of behavioral family based treatment for obese children. *Journal of American Medical Association, 264:* 2519-2524.

Institute of Medicine (IOM). (2002). *Dietary Reference Intakes for Energy, Carbohydrates, Fiber, Fat, Protein and Amino acids (macronutrients): National Academy of Sciences, Institute of Medicine.* Washington, DC: IOM.

Lohman, T.G. (1992). *Advances in body composition.* Champaign, IL: Human Kinetics.

Meredith, M.D., & Welk, G.J. (2005). *FITNESSGRAM/ ACTIVITYGRAM test administration manual (3rd ed.).* Champaign, IL: Human Kinetics.

Mohnsen, B. (1994). *Concepts of physical education.* Reston, VA: NASPE.

Newman, K. (2004). Why are we so fat? *National Geographic, 206*(2), 46-61.

U.S. Department of Agriculture. (2005). *MyPyramid.gov.* Pueblo, Co: Superintendent of Documents. (www.mypyramid.gov)

Websites

Department of Agriculture Food Guide Pyramid   www.MyPyramid.gov

American Dietetic Association   www.eatright.org

National Dairy Council - Tools for Schools
www.nationaldairycouncil.org/nationaldairycouncil/tools

Chapter 13
Muscular Strength and Endurance

A quality physical education program provides positive experiences through which children can assess, achieve and maintain muscular strength and endurance throughout the year. Muscular strength and endurance activities are to be fun and are to promote each child's perception of competence about his ability to perform muscular strength and endurance.

Muscular and muscular endurance are two separate but interrelated fitness components. Because they are interrelated and are developed in children by performing many of the same exercises, the concepts and activities for these two components have been combined into one chapter. The contents of this chapter are organized as follows:

♥ Muscular Strength and Endurance Concepts
♥ Muscular Strength and Endurance Activities

MUSCULAR STRENGTH AND ENDURANCE CONCEPTS

The concepts in this chapter apply specifically to muscular strength and endurance and are organized into "what's," "why's," and "how's." Teaching these concepts is as important as the muscular strength and endurance activities themselves; with these understandings, students may be motivated to incorporate strength and endurance exercises into their physical activities outside the school setting. It may be helpful to read through all the concepts before selecting one or two for each lesson.

The "*Whats*" of Muscular Strength and Endurance

1. ***What is the definition of muscular strength?*** Muscular strength is the largest amount of force one can put forth, through the recruitment of muscle fibers, to overcome a resistance <u>one time</u>. An example of strength is how many pounds of library books he can lift just one time.

2. ***What is the definition of muscular endurance?*** Muscular endurance is one's ability to use the muscles <u>repeatedly</u>. An example of muscular endurance is how many pounds of library books not only can be lifted, but can be carried all the way home. One's level of muscular endurance determines how long his muscles will continue to work before fatiguing.

3. ***What is a healthy level of muscular strength and endurance?*** A healthy level of muscular strength and endurance allows one to participate in moderate to vigorous activity with minimal risk of injury. Different activities require strength and endurance of different muscle groups; in-line skating involves primarily the leg muscles while swimming involves both the leg and the arm and shoulder girdle muscles. An excessive amount of muscular strength and endurance, as is often developed by professional body builders, is not necessary for good health.

4. ***What are muscles?*** Muscles are tissues made up of millions of tiny fibers. The fibers in each muscle are grouped into motor units; each motor unit is connected by nerve pathways to the brain. The brain, via the nerve pathways, informs the muscles as to how many motor units are needed to perform various tasks. For example, more motor units are required to lift a book than are required to lift a pencil.

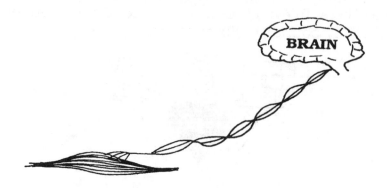

5. ***What happens to muscle fibers when they are exercised regularly?***
The individual muscle fibers get larger when exercised regularly.

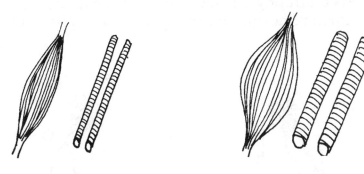

Unexercised Muscle Fibers   **Exercised Muscle Fibers**

6. ***What are the FITT Guidelines for muscular strength and endurance?***
F = Frequency. Perform muscular strength and endurance exercises for each muscle group two to three days per week.

I = Intensity. Intensity is determined by the amount of weight and the number of repetitions. Strength exercises are usually characterized by more intensity (weight) and fewer repetitions (less time) than muscular endurance exercises. Optimal intensity is reached when one feels a slight pull in the muscles without excessive strain.

T = Time. Strength exercises may have greater intensity (weight) and fewer repetitions (less time) than endurance exercises although total time exercising may be similar. Each muscular strength and endurance exercise segment of a physical education lesson may last from three to five minutes.

T = Type. Perform activities and exercises that work the specific muscle group to be developed. The same exercises may be used to develop muscular strength and muscular endurance of a muscle group; however, strength exercises may have greater intensity (weight) and fewer repetitions (less time) than endurance exercises.

7. ***What are some major muscles that can benefit from muscular strength and endurance exercises?*** The deltoid, pectoral, tricep, bicep, and rectus abdominis are some major muscles that can be developed through strength and endurance exercises. Appendix A1 illustrates the location of major muscles in the body.

- ♥ ***The Deltoid*** is the muscle covering the shoulder joint. Delta means "triangle;" the deltoid is shaped like a triangle.

- ♥ ***The Pectoral*** muscles are located in the chest.

- ♥ ***The Triceps*** are located along the back of the upper arm. "Tri" means three; the triceps have three parts.

- ♥ ***The Biceps*** are located on the front of the upper arm. "Bi" means two; the biceps have two parts.

- ♥ ***The Rectus Abdominis*** is the stomach muscle.

8. ***What happens to the muscles when they are not used?*** Muscles that are not used become weak. When muscles become flabby from not being used, it is called atrophy. People who wear a cast for several weeks will notice that, upon removing the cast, the muscles have atrophied from lack of use.

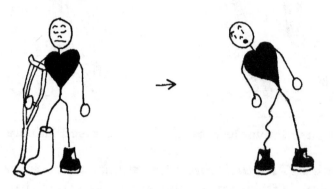

9. ***What is the difference between the strength of boys and girls?*** Until approximately age 12, girls can develop just as much strength as boys! In most children the hormone testosterone, which allows boys to develop stronger and larger muscles, has not yet appeared. Additionally, some people believe women should not attempt to increase their strength because their muscles will become big and ugly. This is not true; the hormones in women's bodies make it impossible for them to become "muscle bound." When women perform strength exercises, their muscles become stronger and firmer, and just a little bit bigger.

10. ***What is the difference between muscular strength and endurance exercises for children and those for adults?*** Both children and adults need to develop muscular strength and endurance. In children, the focus is on developing strength and endurance through similar activities involving lifting their own body weight; push-ups and curl-ups are examples of these activities. In adults, after bone growth is complete, weights can be used to develop muscular strength and endurance. To develop strength, more weight and fewer repetitions are performed; to develop endurance, less weight and more repetitions are performed.

The "*Why*" of Muscular Strength and Endurance

Why is muscular strength and endurance important?

♥   Strength and endurance help prevent injuries like muscle pulls and strains.

♥   Strength and endurance in the upper body and abdominal muscles help to reduce low back pain and maintain good posture.

♥   Strength helps bones become stronger and may reduce one's risk of osteoporosis.

♥   Strength and endurance are also important because strong muscles make it easier to learn skills.

♥   Strength and endurance help us to be more active!

The "*How's*" of Muscular Strength and Endurance

1.   **How many bones and muscles are there in the body?** There are 206 bones and over 600 muscles in the body!

2.   ***How do muscles work?*** Muscles get shorter when they contract. Muscles get longer (they lengthen) when they relax. The action of the biceps muscle is one example. When the biceps are contracted (arm is flexed), the biceps get shorter. When the biceps are relaxed (arm is extended), the biceps get longer.

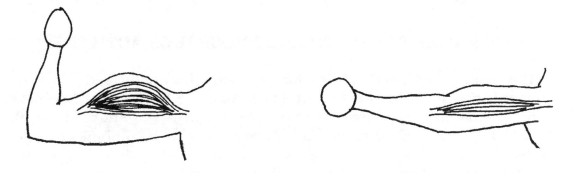

3.   ***How do the principles of exercise apply to muscular strength and endurance?***

Overload. Lift a little more weight than the muscles are accustomed to increase muscular strength. Increase the number of repetitions of the exercise to develop muscular endurance.

Progression. Initially, lift a portion of the body weight for five to ten seconds or approximately five to ten repetitions. Gradually increase time or intensity (weight).

Specificity. Perform exercises using the specific muscle group to be developed. Exercises aimed at increasing the strength and endurance of the abdominal muscles will have little or no effect on the strength and endurance of the muscles in the arm and shoulder girdle region.

Regularity. Perform muscular strength and endurance exercises at least two days per week. Avoid exercising the same muscles strenuously on consecutive days.

Individual Differences. Everybody is unique due to differences in body fat, nutrition, health, motivation, and genetic make-up. Do not compare students' levels of muscular strength and endurance; encourage each child to exercise at her own pace and to achieve levels of muscular strength and endurance within the Healthy Fitness Zone.

4. ***How are muscular strength and endurance measured?*** The push-up measures upper body strength and endurance, the curl-up measures abdominal strength and endurance, and the trunk lift measures trunk extensor strength and flexibility (*Cooper Institute for Aerobics Research, 2005)*. The curl-up and push-up are explained in this chapter; the trunk lift is described in Chapter 14. There is not one general measurement of muscular strength and endurance; a different assessment item is used to measure each muscle group.

MUSCULAR STRENGTH AND ENDURANCE ACTIVITIES

The muscular strength and endurance activities are divided into two sections: ***Individual Exercises and Activities***. The ***Individual Exercises*** section is separated into exercises to develop the **arm and shoulder girdle** region and the **abdominal** region; the ***Activities*** section combines exercises to develop both of these areas. The √ sign is used to identify guidelines for performing each activity correctly. Teachers may select from either of the two sections; however, activities for both the arm and shoulder girdle and the abdominal regions are included in every lesson. Strength and endurance of the leg muscles are developed through cardiovascular fitness activities; therefore, leg strength and endurance are not included in this chapter.

The terms, **sets and repetitions**, are used in this chapter. A set is a specific number of repetitions. For example, the statement, "two sets of ten repetitions" indicates that the students will perform an exercise ten times, rest briefly, and perform the exercise ten times once again.

When teaching the following activities, the process of participation in muscular strength and endurance exercises is more important than the product of a healthy level of strength and endurance. The process needs to be fun and one in which all students feel confident and competent about their ability to perform muscular strength and endurance activities.

Individual Exercises

This section includes strength and endurance exercises for the muscles of the **arm and shoulder girdle** and the **abdominal** regions. Exercises to develop each muscle group are included in each lesson.

Muscular Strength and Endurance Exercises for the Arm and Shoulder Girdle Region

This section contains twenty exercises that develop strength and endurance of the muscles of the upper body. The exercises are organized in progression, starting with arm circles and ending with the pull-up. Exercises eleven through fourteen are simple lead-ups to prepare students to perform a push-up, the *FITNESSGRAM/ACTIVITYGRAM* manual's recommended test of upper body strength and endurance, correctly. The following instructional cues will help students to perform each exercise properly:

♥   Maintain good posture and without arching or rounding the back.

♥   Tighten the abdominal muscles by pulling the belly button into spine.

♥   Exercise in a slow and controlled manner without jerking or bouncing.

1.   ARM CIRCLES

Stand with the back straight, head up, and feet shoulder width apart. Extend the arms out to the side and circle forward and backward.

√   Avoid locking the elbows.

♥   Two sets of 5 to 10 repetitions each direction, palms up

♥   Two sets of 5 to 10 repetitions each direction, palms down

2.   BICEP CURL

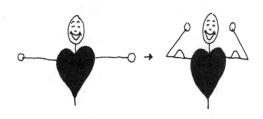

Stand with arms extended out to the side, palms up. First contract the biceps by tightening the bicep muscles and bending the arms. Then slowly extend both arms. Keep the upper arms parallel to the ground.

♥   Two sets of 10 to 20 repetitions

3.   WINDSHIELD WIPER

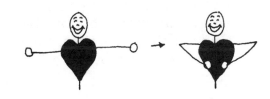

Stand with the arms extended out to the side, palms down. First, bring hands in toward the body by bending at the elbow. Then use the triceps to extend the arms. Keep upper arms parallel to the ground.

♥   Two sets of 10 to 20 repetitions

4. DOORKNOB

Stand with the arms out to the side, palms facing down. Rotate the wrists forward and backward while keeping the arms parallel to the ground.

♥ Two sets of 10 to 20 repetitions

5. LONG BRIDGE

Begin by crouching with the hands touching the ground. Walk the hands out as far as possible. Walk the hands back in toward the feet and return to the starting position.

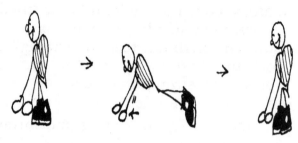

√ Avoid arching or rounding the back.
♥ 2 sets of 3 to 5 repetitions

6. MEASURING WORM

Start in the push-up position. Keep the legs straight and inch the feet in as close to the hands as possible. Return to the push-up position by walking the hands forward.

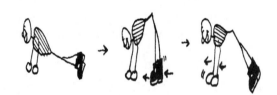

√ Avoid arching or rounding the back.
♥ 2 sets of 3 to 5 repetitions

7. PUPPY DOG WALK

Bend over and place the hands on the ground with the arms and legs slightly bent. Keep the head up and move in all directions.

♥ Move continuously for 5 to 15 seconds

8. BEAR WALK

Start in puppy dog walk position. Move hand and foot on the same side at the same time. Keep the head up and move in all directions.

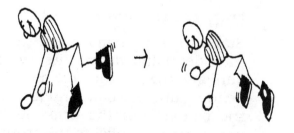

♥ Move continuously for 5 to 15 seconds

9. RABBIT JUMP

Begin by crouching with the hands touching the ground, arms inside of the knees. Reach forward with both ground, jump forward with the feet hands. After hands are placed on the and resume the starting position.

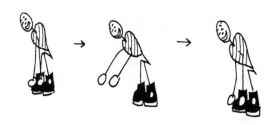

♥   2 sets of 5 to 10 jumps

10. TREADMILL

Place the hands on the ground, shoulder width apart. Extend the **right** leg back. Bend the **left** knee to a 90 degree angle so the sole of the **left** foot rests on the floor. Keeping the hands on the ground, switch the positions of the legs so the **left** leg is straight and the **right** knee is bent.

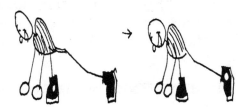

√   Avoid arching or rounding the back.

♥   2 sets of 3 to 10 repetitions
♥   Count one repetition each time the **right** foot is forward

11. WALL PUSH-UP

Place the hands against a wall, shoulder width apart. Keeping the body straight, bend the elbows to bring the chest close to the wall.

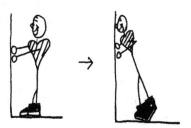

√   Avoid arching or rounding the back.

♥   2 sets of 5 to 10 repetitions

12. CHAIR PUSH-UP

Place a chair against a wall. Position the hands on the edge of the seat, shoulder width apart. Keep the back straight and lower the body until the chest touches the seat of the chair.

√   Avoid arching or rounding the back.

♥   2 sets of 2 to 10 repetitions

13. FLAT TIRE

Begin in a modified or regular push-up position with the arms straight. As the body is slowly lowered, the students make a sound that resembles air leaking from a tire. Rest chest on floor. Push back up slowly.

√ Avoid arching or rounding the back.

♥ 2 sets of 5 to 10 repetitions

♥ Variation: Begin in a regular push-up position or avoid resting chest on floor for a more advanced level.

14. BENT-KNEE or MODIFIED PUSH-UP

Lie face down on the floor. Place the hands on the floor along side the shoulders. Push the upper body up while leaving the knees on the ground. The chin touches the ground each time the body is lowered.

√ Avoid arching or rounding the back.

♥ 2 sets of 5 to 10 repetitions

15. PUSH-UP

Begin in a prone position, knees off the floor, hands under the shoulders, fingers pointing straight ahead. Lower the body so the elbows at a 90 degree angle. Push back up to the starting position.

√ Avoid arching or rounding the back.

♥ 2 sets of 2 to 10 repetitions

♥ The push-up is a recommended test for upper body strength and endurance in *FITNESSGRAM/ACTIVITYGRAM*. Students perform as many push-ups as possible to a cadence of one per three seconds (*FITNESSGRAM/ACTIVITYGRAM* CD).

16. MODIFIED PULL-UP

Use a low (waist high) horizontal bar with an elastic band placed 7 to 8 inches below and parallel to the bar.
Lying on the back, grasp the bar with the palms facing away from the body, shoulder width apart. Begin with straight arms and legs, only heels touching the ground. Pull up until the chin is above the elastic band.

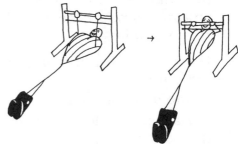

√   Keep body straight – only arms move.
♥   2 sets of 2 to 10 repetitions
♥   The modified pull-up is an alternate test for upper body strength and endurance in *FITNESSGRAM/ACTIVITYGRAM*. Students complete as many modified pull-ups as possible.

17. FLEXED ARM HANG

Hold on to a horizontal bar with the palms facing away from the body. Jump (or get a boost!) up so the chin is above the bar, elbows are bent and chest is close to the bar. Hang with the chin above the bar as long as possible.

√   Do not rest the chin on the bar.
√   The body must not swing.
√   Students with a low level of upper body strength are not to attempt this exercise as the chin may hit the bar.

♥   Hold for 1 to 30 seconds
♥   The flexed arm hang is an alternate test for upper body strength and endurance in *FITNESSGRAM/ACTIVITYGRAM*. Students hang with the chin above the bar for as many seconds as possible.

18. CHIN-UP

Grasp a horizontal bar with the palms facing toward the body. Keeping the body straight, bend the arms, and pull the body up until the chin is above the bar. Slowly lower the body until the arms are straight.

♥   2 sets of 1 to 10 repetitions

19. ROPE CLIMB

Begin by grasping the rope as high as possible. Use the hand over hand method to ascend the rope. The feet may be wrapped around the rope if the rope cannot be climbed using the arms alone.

√ Use the hand under hand method to descend the rope to avoid rope burns.

♥ Climb as far as possible in 10 to 30 seconds

♥ Variation: A pole may be climbed by using the arms only or by "pinching" the pole with the soles of the feet. A pole is more difficult to climb than a rope.

20. PULL-UP

Grasp a horizontal bar with the palms facing away from the body and hang with the feet above the ground. Keeping the body straight, bend the arms and pull the body up until the chin is above the bar. Slowly lower the body until the arms are straight; the feet do not touch the ground.

√ Avoid kicking and jerking.

♥ 2 sets of 1 to 10 repetitions

♥ The pull-up is an alternate test for upper body strength and endurance in *FITNESSGRAM/ACTIVITYGRAM*. Students complete as many pull-ups as possible.

Muscular Strength and Endurance Exercises for the Abdominal Region

This section contains seven exercises that develop abdominal strength and endurance. The exercises are organized in progression, starting with bicycle pedaling and ending with the plank. The first four exercises are simple lead-ups to prepare students to perform a curl-up, the test of abdominal strength and endurance included in *FITNESSGRAM/ACTIVITYGRAM*, correctly. The following instructional cues will help students to perform each exercise correctly:

♥ Tighten the abdominal muscles by pulling the belly button into spine during the entirety of each exercise.

♥ Exercise in a slow and controlled manner without jerking or bouncing.

♥ Maintain good posture and without arching or rounding the back.

1.   BICYCLE PEDALING

Sit with knees bent and feet flat on floor. Lean backward and rest elbows on the ground. Raise feet, point toes, and alternate pushing each foot forward.

√   Pedal in a slow and controlled manner.
√   Pull belly button into spine.

♥   2 sets of 5 to 10 repetitions
♥   Count one repetition each time the **right** foot is forward.

2.   SIT-BACK

Sit with knees bent at a 140 degree angle, arms along side of the body, palms down. Slowly lean backward until the head touches the ground. Perform an assisted sit up (see below) to return to the starting position.

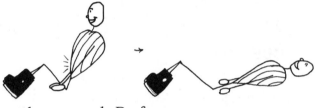

√   Sit back in a slow and controlled manner.
√   Pull belly button into spine.

♥   2 sets of 5 to 10 repetitions

3.   ASSISTED SIT-UP

Lie with knees bent at a 140 degree angle, arms along side the body, palms down. Hold on to the hamstrings (back of the thighs), and slowly pull the body to an upright position. Perform a sit-back (see above) to return to the starting position.

√   Sit up in a slow and controlled manner.
√   Pull belly button into spine.

♥   2 sets of 5 to 10 repetitions

4. SIT AND HOLD

Place arms at side, palms down. Curl up until the shoulder blades are just off the floor and hold this position. Students may count out loud the number of seconds the position is to be held. The name of one major abdominal muscle is the rectus abdominis; the students may count the seconds by saying: "1-rectus abdominis, 2-rectus abdominis, 3-rectus abdominis!"

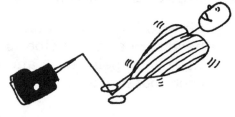

√ Lift body in a slow and controlled manner.
√ Pull belly button into spine.

♥ Three sets of one repetition
♥ A repetition consists of holding the position for 3 to 5 seconds

5. CURL-UP

Lie on back with knees at a 140-degree angle (adjust the location of heels appropriately), soles of feet on the floor. Place arms at side, palms down. Curl up until the shoulder blades are just off the floor. Curl back down until head touches the floor.

√ Curl up in a slow and controlled manner.
√ Pull belly button into spine.
√ Feet are not help on curl-ups.

♥ The curl-up is the recommended test for abdominal strength and endurance in *FITNESSGRAM/ACTIVITYGRAM*. A curl-up strip is placed at student's fingertips; the width of the strip depends on the student's age (3 inches for ages 5-9 and 4.5 inches for ages 9 and above). The student curls up slowly, sliding his fingertips across the measuring strip until the fingertips reach the other side, then curls back down until his head touches the mat (or partner's hands). Students perform as many curl-ups as possible with a maximum of 75, to a cadence of one every three seconds. The cadence is recorded on the *FITNESSGRAM/ACTIVITYGRAM* CD.

6. KNEE LIFT

Hang from a horizontal bar with the arms straight. Bend the knees. Lift one knee until the thigh is parallel with the ground. Alternate the **right** and **left** knee.

√   Lift knees in a slow and controlled manner.

√   Pull belly button into spine.

♥   2 sets of 5 to 10 repetitions

♥   Count one repetition each time the **right** knee is lifted

♥   Variation: Lift both knees at the same time.

7. PLANK

Lie face down with forearms on the floor, hands clasped. Keep the elbows directly below the shoulders. Lift hips off floor. Keeping the back straight, hold this isometric exercise.

√   Keep back straight.

√   Pull belly button into spine.

♥   3 sets of 1 repetition

♥   A repetition consists of holding the plank for 3 to 5 seconds

♥   Variation: Lift knees off floor and hold.

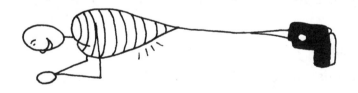

Activities

This section contains seven activities that may be used to develop upper body and abdominal strength and endurance. With the exception of Exercises to Music, detailed instructions for each of the following activities are found in Chapter 11. Exercises to Music, an activity similar to Rhythmic Aerobic Exercise, is described in detail. The exercises performed in these activities are found in the **Individual Exercises** section of this chapter.

1. CIRCUIT TRAINING

The stations may include two sets of the following exercises.

Push-Up (modified or regular)	**Arm Circles**	**Long Bridge**
Sit Back	**Measuring Worm**	**Curl-up**
Assisted Sit-up	**Bicycle Pedaling**	**Chair Push-up**

The students perform the exercises at each station at their own pace. Each circuit training sign may contain three levels of difficulty.

2. FOUR-CORNERS MOVEMENT

A 10' X 10' square is suggested as many muscular strength and endurance movements are fairly slow, and large boundaries may discourage students. Additionally, two separate Four-Corners courses may be used to avoid crowding. A passing lane may be designated around the outside. Six or Eight-Corners Movement may also be used. The following movements are suggested.

1. Puppy Dog Walk	**3. Bear Walk**
2. Walk and Use Arms	**4. Walk and Use Arms**

Two of these movements require the arms to support the body weight. Intersperse periods of rest throughout the activity. Abdominal exercises and walking or jogging may be added at various intervals to give the arms and shoulders a rest.

3. New Leader Exercises

The students are given a list of acceptable exercises that may include the following.

Arm Circles	**Push-up (modified or regular)**	**Treadmill**
Curl-up	**Long Bridge**	**Plank**
Sit and Hold	**Animal Movements (Puppy Dog Walk, Bear Walk or Measuring Worm)**	

4.   Challenge Courses

All of the Challenge Courses described in Chapter 11 may be modified for muscular strength and endurance development by including the following movements.

Bicycle Pedaling	**Windshield Wiper**	**Curl-up**
Bear Walk	**Student Choice??**	**Sit and Hold**

Signs with the names of specific exercises may be set up against cones. Students complete the designated movement for the appropriate amount of seconds before moving to the next cone.

CURL-UP *10 seconds*	***SIT AND HOLD*** *10 seconds*

5.   Astronaut Drills

Astronaut Drills adapt easily to muscular strength and endurance development. Walking is interspersed with the following movements.

Puppy Dog Walk	**Push-up (modified or regular)**	**Rabbit Jump**
Bicycle Pedaling	**Assisted Sit-up**	**Curl-up**

6.   Squad Leader Exercises

The leaders may be given a list of muscular strength and endurance exercises. Each squad leader is responsible for leading two or three students in a routine that may consist of the following activities.

Arm Circles	**Bicycle Pedaling**	**Flat Tire**
Plank	**Curl-up**	**Wall Push-up***

*When a wall is available, utilize the wall push-up as often as possible.

7.   Exercises to Music

This activity is described in detail because it is not found in Chapter 11.

Description

Exercises to Music is a muscular strength and endurance activity similar to Rhythmic Aerobics. A variety of individual muscular strength and endurance exercises are performed. The students exercise on towels or mats whenever appropriate. Continuous background music may be used.

Organization

The students are spread out in a scattered formation within the boundaries. The boundaries are large enough that students can move freely within them.

Sample Beginning Routine: Exercises to Music

1. Bicycle Pedaling--5 seconds
2. Push-up (modified or regular)--5 seconds
3. Stop and name the muscles being used! (pectorals, deltoids, rectus abdominis)
4. Curl-up--5 seconds
5. Long Bridge--5 seconds
6. Plank--5 seconds
7. Repeat these exercises or add new ones
8. Provide intermittent opportunities for stretching or walking in place (5 to 10 seconds)

Because some students take longer than others to complete a specific number of repetitions, use a time limit for most exercises. Ask the students to try to complete as many quality repetitions of each exercise as possible within a certain number of seconds. If the teacher requires a specific number of repetitions, some students may be able to perform more while others may perform less. The "no-wait" method of using seconds instead of repetitions helps to insure quality execution of movements, prevents embarrassment and allows all students to be challenged.

Summary

The concepts related to muscular strength and endurance, as well as the strength and endurance exercises and activities, are essential elements of a physical education lesson. Healthy levels of muscular strength and endurance, developed at an early age and maintained throughout one's lifetime, allow one to regularly participate in moderate to vigorous activity and will enhance one's quality of life.

References

Cooper Institute for Aerobics Research. (2005). *FITNESSGRAM/ACTIVITYGRAM test administration manual.* Champaign, IL: Human Kinetics.

Corbin, C.B., Lindsey, R., & Welk, G.J. (2002*). Concepts of physical fitness* (11th ed.). St. Louis: McGraw-Hill.

Franks, B.D., Corbin, C., & Pangrazi, B. (2000). Definitions: Health, fitness, and physical activity. *President's Council on Physical Fitness and Sports Research Digest, 8*(1), 1-6.

Howley, E.T., & Franks, B.D. (1997). *Health fitness instructor's guide.* Champaign, IL: Human Kinetics.

Leihmon, W., Haydu, T., & Phillips, D. (1999). Questionable exercises. *President's Council on Physical Fitness and Sports Research Digest, 7*(4), 1-6.

Pangrazi, R. (2007). *Dynamic physical education for elementary school children* (15th ed.). San Francisco, CA: Pearson Publishing.

Roberts, S.O., & Pillarella, D. (1996). *Developing strength in children: A comprehensive guide.* Reston, VA: NASPE.

USDHHS. (1996). *Physical activity and health: A report of the surgeon general.* Atlanta, GA: USDHHS, CDC, National Center for Chronic Disease Prevention and Health Promotion.

Chapter 14
Flexibility

A quality health related physical fitness-based physical education program provides positive experiences through which children can achieve, maintain and assess flexibility throughout the year. Flexibility activities are to be fun, and are to promote each child's perception of competence about his ability to perform flexibility exercises. The chapter is organized as follows:

♥ Flexibility Concepts
♥ Flexibility Exercises

FLEXIBILITY CONCEPTS

The concepts in this chapter apply specifically to flexibility and are organized into "what's," "why's," and "how's." Teaching these concepts is as important as the flexibility activities themselves; with these understandings, students may be motivated to incorporate flexibility exercises into their physical activities outside the school setting. It may be helpful to read through all of the concepts before selecting one or two for inclusion in each lesson.

The "*What's*" of Flexibility

1. ***What is the definition of flexibility?*** Flexibility is the range of movement of a specific joint or group of joints and the corresponding muscle groups. For example, riding a bicycle requires a range of movement in the knee joint and requires flexibility of the hamstring muscles. A person may be quite flexible in one joint motion, but inflexible in another joint. Most physical activities require a certain amount of flexibility.

2. ***What is a healthy level of flexibility?*** A healthy level of flexibility is a normal level that allows one to participate in moderate to vigorous physical activity with minimal risk of injury. Very high or low levels of flexibility may represent an increased risk of injury.

3. ***What are the three types of stretching?*** The three types of stretching are: static, ballistic, and P.N.F. (Proprioceptive Neuromuscular Facilitation).

♥ ***Static stretching*** is slowly stretching a muscle until it becomes a little longer than its normal length, and holding it in that position. Static stretching is preferred to ballistic stretching because there is less danger of injury and muscle soreness; thus, static stretches are included in this chapter.

♥ ***Ballistic stretching*** involves bobbing, bouncing, or jerking movements. Ballistic stretching may cause injury and is not recommended for use with children.

♥ ***Proprioceptive neuromuscular facilitation (P.N.F.) stretching*** involves a Contract-Relax-Contract sequence that is advanced and is not within the scope of this book.

4. ***What are the FITT Guidelines for flexibility?***

   F = Frequency. Perform flexibility exercises three to seven days per week, and always after moderate or vigorous physical activity (MVPA).

   I = Intensity. Slowly stretch until mild discomfort is felt and back off slightly before holding the stretch.

   T = Time. Perform stretching exercises for two to five minutes following MVPA. Perform four to five stretches for each major muscle group used in activity; repeat each stretch several times. Hold each stretch for 15 to 30 seconds (five to 15 seconds with young children). Light stretching may also be performed prior to MVPA; however, only stretch muscles that have been thoroughly warmed up. Flexibility exercises are usually performed for two to three minutes at the conclusion of the lesson.

   T = Type. Perform static exercises that stretch the muscles slowly. Avoid bouncing or jerky movements.

5. ***What is the largest joint in the body?*** The knee joint is the largest joint in the body. It is located between two long bones, the femur in the upper leg and the tibia in the lower leg. It can experience a lot of force, and can be injured when certain exercises are performed incorrectly.

6. ***What is the difference between the flexibility of children and the flexibility of adults?*** Most children have adequate levels of flexibility; however, flexibility tends to decrease as people become older. Flexibility decreases with age when people do not stretch on a regular basis; therefore, it becomes more important to stretch regularly, and especially following participation in moderate to vigorous physical activity, as we age.

7. ***What is overstretching?*** When a muscle is stretched too far, the stretch reflex is activated. The stretch reflex causes a muscle that is being overstretched to tighten up to avoid injury; overstretching can actually tighten muscles rather than loosen them! Reach to the point of discomfort and back off slightly before holding the stretch to avoid overstretching.

The "W*hy's*" of Flexibility

1. ***Why is flexibility important?*** Flexibility is needed for safe and effective movement. It is important to develop flexibility in all areas of the body to carry out a physically active lifestyle. Healthy levels of flexibility are needed to minimize risk of injury during moderate to vigorous physical activities. Stretching also helps to relieve muscle cramps and may prevent muscle soreness.

2. ***Why do people seem to become less flexible as we age?*** A decrease in flexibility as we age is largely due to decreased participation in stretching and physical activity. Stretching exercises can benefit people of all ages!

The "*How's*" of Flexibility

1. ***How are flexibility exercises incorporated into the physical education lesson?*** Flexibility exercises are usually performed at the conclusion of the lesson following moderate to vigorous physical activity. Four to five stretches are performed for each of the major muscle groups used. Light stretching may be performed earlier in the lesson; however, muscles must be thoroughly warmed up before any stretches are performed.

2. ***How is breathing involved in stretching?*** It is important to breathe while stretching. It sounds silly but some people hold their breath while they stretch.

Exhale while reaching.

Breathe normally while holding the stretch.

Inhale while releasing.

3. ***How are the knees positioned when stretching?*** Avoid locking the knees while stretching because locking may cause stress to the sensitive knee joint that may result in injury. Locking the knees may also place stress on the low back.

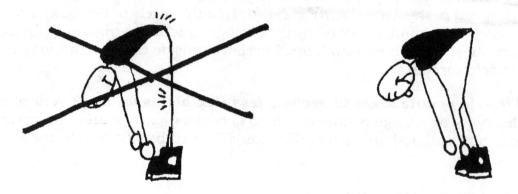

4. ***How does one bend forward properly when stretching?*** When reaching forward from a standing or sitting position, bend from the hips keeping the back straight. Rounding the upper back may lead to poor posture. One way to keep the back straight is to keep the head up while stretching.

5. ***How do the Principles of Exercise apply to flexibility?***

Overload. Stretch muscles a little bit farther each time to become more flexible (increased intensity). The frequency of stretching sessions, as well as the time each stretch is held may also be increased. A higher than normal flexibility level, however, is not necessary, nor is it desirable.

Progression. Begin by holding each stretch for five seconds. Work up to holding each stretch for 10 to 15 seconds.

Specificity. To develop flexibility of a specific joint and its corresponding muscle groups, stretch the muscles in that specific region regularly. For example, to develop flexibility of the hamstring muscles, perform exercises aimed at stretching the hamstrings. Exercises aimed at developing flexibility of the muscles in the arm and shoulder girdle region will have little or no effect upon the flexibility of the hamstrings. An individual may be quite flexible in one joint motion but inflexible in another joint.

Regularity. Perform flexibility exercises three to seven days per week, and always following moderate to vigorous physical activity. Ideally, perform stretching exercises on a daily basis.

Individual Differences. Every person is unique due to differences in genetic make-up, health, nutrition, body fat, and motivation. Do not compare different children's levels of flexibility; encourage each child to progress at her own rate and to achieve a level of flexibility within the Healthy Fitness Zone.

6. *How is flexibility developed and maintained?* To become more flexible, stretch the muscles slowly. Avoid jerking or bouncing. Always stretch after participating in moderate to vigorous activity. Try to stretch at least three days per week.

7. *How is flexibility measured?* *FITNESSGRAM* recommends the back saver sit and reach to measure hamstring flexibility and the trunk lift to measure trunk extensor strength and flexibility; these two items are described later in this chapter. There is not one general measurement for flexibility.

FLEXIBILITY EXERCISES

This section contains static stretching exercises aimed at developing flexibility of the major joints and their corresponding muscle groups. The √ sign identifies guidelines for performing each exercise correctly.

The exercises are divided into two categories: **Upper Body Flexibility Exercises and Lower Body Flexibility Exercises**. The teacher selects exercises from both categories to include in each lesson; however, it is important that the specific muscle groups used during moderate to vigorous activity are stretched following activity. Some exercises requiring students to lie on the ground may not be feasible on certain surfaces, and may need to be modified or eliminated if mats, carpets, or towels are not available.

When teaching flexibility exercises, the process of participation in the exercises is more important than the product of a healthy level of flexibility. The process needs to be fun and one in which all students feel confident and competent about their ability to perform flexibility activities.

Upper Body Flexibility Exercises

This section consists of eleven exercises to develop upper body flexibility. The following instructional cues will help students to perform each stretch correctly:

- ♥ Maintain good posture; pull the shoulders back and the belly button in toward the spine.
- ♥ Avoid arching (except in the trunk lift) or rounding the back and locking the knees or the elbows.
- ♥ Exercise in a slow and controlled manner without jerking or bouncing.
- ♥ Breathe deeply while stretching.

1. NECK ROTATOR

Tilt the head to the **left** and hold, return to the center. Tilt the head to the **right** and hold.

- √ Never roll the head back. This motion may pinch a nerve.
- √ If your neck hurts, move your neck a different way so it does not hurt.
- ♥ Hold each tilt for 4 seconds
- ♥ Repeat 2 to 3 times
- ♥ Variation: Look to the **left**, look to the **right**, and gently pull your chin toward your chest.

2. SINGLE SHOULDER SHRUG

Lift one shoulder at a time up and down, alternating between **right** and **left** shoulders.

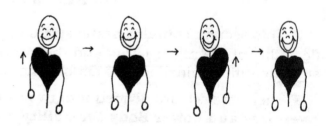

- ♥ Repeat for 8 to 16 counts
- ♥ Variation: Lift both shoulders at the same time

3. ARM RAISE

Reach arms upward and slightly backward.

- √ Avoid locking the elbows.
- ♥ Hold for 5 to 20 seconds
- ♥ Repeat 2 to 3 times

4.   ARM CIRCLES

Stand with the back straight,
head up, and feet shoulder width
apart. Extend the arms, bent
slightly at the elbow, out to the side
and circle forward and backward.

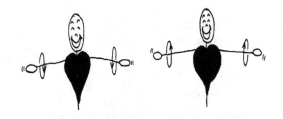

- ♥   Two sets of 5 to 10 repetitions in each direction, palms up
- ♥   Two sets of 5 to 10 repetitions in each direction, palms down

5.   SWIMMER

Tilt the trunk forward slightly.
Imitate the free-style swim
stroke with the arms.

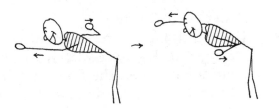

- ♥   Complete 10 to 12 "strokes"

6.   TRICEPS STRETCH

Bend the **right** elbow behind
the head. Gently pull the elbow
to the left with the **left** hand.

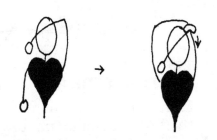

- √   Avoid putting pressure directly on the elbow.
- ♥   Hold for 5 to 20 seconds
- ♥   Repeat 1 to 2 times each side

7.   SHOULDER SQUEEZE

Clasp hands behind the back. Lift
the arms up and away from the
back, squeezing shoulder blades
together. Stand up straight and tall.

- √   Avoid locking the elbows.
- ♥   Hold 5 to 20 seconds
- ♥   Repeat 2 to 3 times

8.   SHOULDER STRETCH

Reach the **right** hand over the **right** shoulder and
down the back. At the same time place the **left** hand
behind the back and reach up, trying to touch the
fingers of the **right** hand. Repeat on the **left** side.

- ♥   This is an optional test for upper body flexibility in
  FITNESSGRAM/ACTIVITYGRAM. The student is successful
  if he can touch hands on both sides.

9.   TRUNK LIFT

Lie face down. Place
hands under thighs
(palms up) and point
toes. Lift the chest
slowly off the floor.
Hold chest at highest point for one to two seconds.

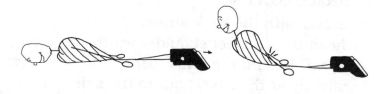

√   Perform trunk lift in a slow and controlled manner.
√   Stop at 12 inches to avoid hyperextending the back.

♥   Repeat 2 to 3 times
♥   The trunk lift is a recommended test for upper body flexibility and
    strength in *FITNESSGRAM/ACTIVITYGRAM*. A ruler is used to measure the
    distance between the floor and the student's chin. Distances greater than
    12 inches are recorded as 12.

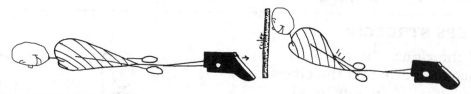

10.   DELTOID STRETCH

Bring the **right** arm across
the body, palm facing toward
the body. Place the **left** hand
above the elbow and pull the
arm toward the body.

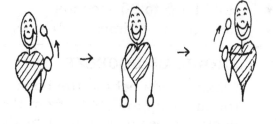

√   Avoid putting pressure directly on
    or locking the elbow.

♥   Hold for 5 to 20 seconds
♥   Repeat 1 to 2 times each arm

11.   WAIST STRETCHER

Reach the **right** arm over the
head.

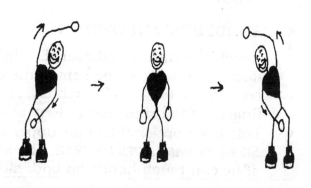

√   Bend to the side; do not tilt
    to the front. Keep the knees
    slightly bent.

♥   Hold for 5 to 20 seconds
♥   Repeat 2 to 4 times each side

Lower Body Flexibility Exercises

This section consists of nine exercises to develop lower body flexibility. The following instructional cues will help students to perform each stretch correctly:

♥   Maintain good posture; pull the shoulders back and the belly button in toward the spine.
♥   When bending the trunk forward, bend from the hips, not the waist or upper back and neck; do not arch or round the back.
♥   Exercise in a slow and controlled manner without jerking or bouncing.
♥   Avoid locking the knees or allowing the angle of the knee to be less than 90 degrees.
♥   Breathe deeply while stretching.

1.   ELONGATION STRETCH

Reach the arms as far as possible in the opposite direction of the feet. Make the body as long as possible!

√   Take deep breaths while holding the stretch.
♥   Hold for 5 to 20 seconds
♥   Repeat 2 to 3 times

2.   LOW BACK STRETCH

Tighten the gluteus maximus (butt) and abdominal (stomach) muscles at the same time. Pull the belly button in toward the spine and push the low back toward the floor.

♥   Hold for 5 to 20 seconds
♥   Repeat 2 to 3 times

3.   PILL BUG

Pull both legs to the chest by holding onto the hamstrings. Push the low back toward the floor.

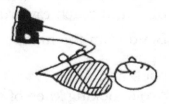

♥   Hold for 5 to 20 seconds
♥   Repeat 2 times each leg
♥   *Variation:* Pull one leg at a time at a time to the chest.

4. HAMSTRING STRETCH

Pull the **right** leg toward the chest (keep right knee slightly bent) by holding on to the hamstrings. The **left** leg is bent and the **left** foot is on the floor.

- ♥ Hold for 5 to 20 seconds
- ♥ Repeat 2 to 3 times

5. BACK-SAVER SIT AND REACH

Seated, extend both legs out in front. Bend the **right** leg and place the sole of the **right** foot on the floor, 2-3 inches to the side of the **left** knee. With hands placed on top of each other, extend the arms forward as far as possible toward the toes. Hold the stretch for 1 to 2 seconds.

√ Reach forward in a slow and controlled manner.

- ♥ Repeat two times each leg
- ♥ The back-saver sit and reach is the recommended test for hamstring flexibility in *FITNESSGRAM/ACTIVITYGRAM*. The student places the sole of the foot of the extended leg against a box with a scale on the top. A ruler is used for the scale and is positioned so that the nine-inch mark is at the point where the foot rests against the box.

6. REVERSE HURDLER'S STRETCH

Seated, extend **right** leg out, knee slightly bent. Place the sole of the **left** foot on the inner thigh of the **right** leg. Bend forward from the hips and reach toward the **right** foot.

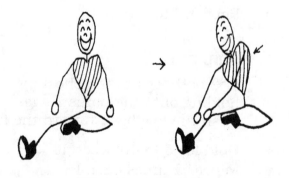

√ Bend from the hips, not the waist or upper
back and neck.

√ Avoid locking knee of straight leg.

- ♥ Hold for 5 to 20 seconds
- ♥ Repeat two times each leg

7.   FORWARD STRIDE STRETCHER

Bend the **right** knee and extend the **left** leg back. Place the hands on the ground, shoulder width apart.

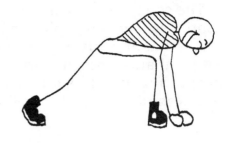

√   The front knee is directly above the ankle. One arm is on each side of the knee. The angle of the knee is not less than 90 degrees.

♥   Hold for 5 to 20 seconds
♥   Repeat two times each leg
♥   *Variation:* Place both arms on the inside of the knee and stretch down as close to the ground as possible.

8.   GASTROCNEMIUS STRETCH

Stand with **right** leg forward, **left** leg back, and toes pointed straight ahead. Bend the **right** knee until a stretch is felt on the back of the lower **left** leg.

√   Keep back heel down and torso upright.
♥   Hold for 5 to 20 seconds
♥   Repeat 2 to 3 times each

9.   TWISTER

Stand with feet shoulder width apart, knees slightly bent. Reach for the **left** foot with the **right** arm. Raise the **left** arm in the air. Bend the knees slightly. Slowly roll up to a standing position.

 → 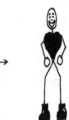 →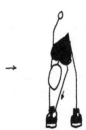

♥   Hold for 5 to 20 seconds
♥   Repeat 2 to 3 times each side

Summary

The concepts related to flexibility, as well as the flexibility exercises, are essential elements of a physical education lesson. Healthy levels of flexibility, developed at an early age and maintained throughout one's lifetime, may greatly enhance one's quality of life. The ultimate goals of teaching flexibility concepts and exercises are to make the activity fun and to allow all students to be successful and develop feelings of competence about their own flexibility.

References

Cooper Institute for Aerobics Research. (2005). *FITNESSGRAM/ ACTIVITYGRAM test administration manual.* Champaign, IL: Human Kinetics.

Corbin, C. B., & Lindsey, R. (1997*). Fitness for life* (4th ed.). Glenview, IL: Scott, Foresman and Company.

Corbin, C. B., & Noble, L. (1985). Flexibility--A major component of physical fitness. In D. Cundiff (Ed.), *Implementation of health fitness exercise programs* (pp. 37-41). Reston, VA: American Alliance for Health, Physical Education, Recreation, and Dance (AAHPERD).

Corbin, C. B., & Pangrazi, B. (1993). The health benefits of physical activity. *President's Council on Physical Fitness and Sports Research Digest, 1*(1), 1-7.

Franks, B.D., Corbin, C., & Pangrazi, B. (2000). Definitions: Health, fitness, and physical activity. *President's Council on Physical Fitness and Sports Research Digest, 8*(1), 1-6.

Holt, J., Holt, L.E., & Pelham, T.W. (1996). Flexibility refined. In T. Bauer (Ed.), *Biomechanics in sports XIII* (pp. 170-174). Thunder Bay, Ontario: Lakehead University.

Jackson, A.W., Morrow, J.R., Brill, P.A., Kohl, H.W., Gordon, N.R., & Blair, S.N. (1998). Relation of sit-up and sit-and-reach tests to lower back pain in adults. *Journal of Orthopaedic and Sports Physical Therapy, 27,* 22-26.

Knudson, D. (1999). Stretching during warm-up: Do we have enough evidence? *JOPERD, 70*(7), 24-27, 51.

Knudson, D.V., Magnesson, P., & McHugh, M. (2000). Current issues in flexibility fitness. *President's Council on Physical Fitness and Sports Research Digest, 3*(10), 1-6.

Liehmon, W., Haydu, T., & Phillips, D. (1999). Questionable exercises. *President's Council on Physical Fitness and Sports Research Digest, 7*(4), 1-6.

Martin, S.B., Jackson, A.W., Morrow, J.R., & Liemohn, W.P. (1998). The rationale for the sit and reach test revisited. *Measurement in Physical Education and Exercise Science, 2,* 85-92.

Sapega, A.A., Quedenfeld, T.C., Moyer, R.A., & Butler, R.A. (1981). Biophysical factors in range-of-motion exercise. *Physician and Sportsmedicine, 12*(9), 57-65.

Chapter 15
Games Without Lines: Everybody Active!

Many popular games, such as kickball and softball, provide minimal opportunity for all children to be active. In other games, such as dodge ball, children as targets; the object is to "peg your peers!" [See the National Association for Sport and Physical Education (NASPE) position statement on dodge ball.] The games included in this chapter provide maximum participation and activity for all students. These active games may be used as a culminating activity, or even as a warm-up, in the physical education lesson. The chapter is divided into three sections:

♥ Team Selection
♥ Using Flags in Active Games
♥ Tag Games

Team Selection

Many of the tag games in this chapter require two or more teams. Team selection is often an embarrassing and humiliating experience for children and can also result in wasted time. The teacher must be sensitive when dividing students into teams. The following grouping or team selection methods are to be avoided.

♥ Avoid allowing captains to select teams. When captains (usually the most skilled students) choose teams, the overfat and unskilled children are the last to be chosen.

♥ Avoid selecting teams based upon gender (boys and girls).

♥ Avoid grouping based upon eye or hair color or any other physical characteristic that would result in cultural bias.

♥ Numbering students is also discouraged; it is time consuming and can become disruptive when students reposition themselves to get the same number as their friend!

♥ Avoid any team selection methods that humiliate or discriminate against students or waste time.

Figure **15.1** lists creative time-efficient approaches to team selection aimed at making all children feel valued.

Figure 15.1 Methods for Selecting Teams

Methods For Selecting Teams

1. By birthdays: **Team #1**= January to June   **Team #2** = July to December
    or **Team #1**= 1st to 15th day   **Team #2** = 16th to 31st day
2. By clothing colors: **Team 1** = blue pants versus other color pants
                          Team 2 = white shoes versus other color shoes
3. By beginning letters of first or last name
4. By ending letters of first or last name
5. By beginning or ending digit of home address
6. By beginning or ending digit of phone number
7. By beginning or ending letter of street name
8. By pets (cats, dogs, fish, etc.)
9. The teacher chooses six to eight equally balanced squads (no more than four students per squad). The squads are combined to form teams:
    Team #1 = squads 2, 4, 6, and 8   **Team #2** = squads 1, 3, 5 and 7
10. By classroom rows
11. By favorite flavor of ice cream, chocolate or vanilla.
12. ??????????????????

Using Flags in Active Games

Flags may be used for three purposes in active games. They may be used to designate tagger(s), to divide the class into teams, and as an alternative to simply "tagging" a player.

Designating the Tagger

Children may become confused during a tag game as to the identity of the "taggers." If the taggers hold a flag in each hand, it is easier for the students to see who is chasing them.

Dividing the Class into Teams

Flags may also be used to divide the class into teams. A teacher with thirty-two students in his class may make flags of eight different colors (four of each color). The flags are spread out within the activity area before class begins. The students are instructed, on a specified signal, to grab one flag as quickly as possible and tuck it into the side of their waistband. After the students have tucked in their flag, the teacher may designate teams based upon flag colors. For example, if two teams are needed for the game, the teacher may combine the reds, whites, blues, and yellows into one team. The greens, oranges, browns, and purples constitute the other team. If four teams are needed, two colors of flags may be combined to make each team. Students will eventually catch on to this procedure, and the teacher will need to be creative in using this method!

Using Flags as an Alternative to Tagging

A third use for flags is as an alternative to tagging. Every student in the class has one or two flags tucked into his waistband. The object of the tag game is to pull the flag of the other player instead of simply touching him. This procedure will prevent the common problem of students not admitting to being tagged. If the flags are used to replace tagging, it may be necessary to practice pulling each other's flags prior to starting the game; practicing the pulling of flags may prevent students from grabbing at clothes rather than flags.

Flag Construction

Flags may be constructed inexpensively out of double knit polyester cut into strips four inches wide by eighteen inches long. Two to eight colors of material are recommended for use in designating teams and taggers.

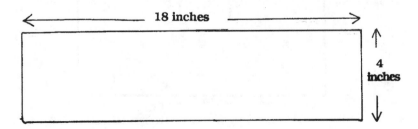

Tag Games

This section explains the rules and organization for 20 tag games designed to promote maximum participation and activity for all students. These games are different from traditional elementary school games in that students are not eliminated when they are tagged; the students who are tagged first are usually the ones who need activity the most! The suggested grade levels for each game are identified next to the title. Games involving teams are not usually appropriate for students in kindergarten through second grade. The games usually last five to seven minutes and are appropriate for use as a culminating activity in a physical education lesson. Additionally, the classroom teacher may use these games during breaks in the school day and on field days.

The games can be modified in numerous ways. One modification is to change the name of the teams; instead of playing Crows and Cranes, call the teams Circles and Squares (primary grades) or Botswana and Burundi (intermediate grades). When modifying rules, insure that NEVER is a child eliminated or taken out of play. Avoid playing a game until only one person remains untagged; stop each game when five to seven students remain untagged. De-emphasize winning at all grade levels; focus on good sportsmanship, having fun and trying one's best. If you had fun, you WON! Having fun, experiencing success and feeling good about one self, and maximal activity time is the focus. Variations for several games are provided.

SPIDERS AND FLIES: Grades K to 3

1. Two students are chosen to be spiders. The remaining players are flies.
2. The spiders encourage the flies to come into the circle as close to the "web" as possible.
3. When the spiders (or the teacher) shout "TRAP," the flies "take off," and attempt to move outside the circle before the spiders tag them (pull their flags).
4. Flies who are tagged (flags are pulled) become spiders.
5. The game continues until four or five flies remain.

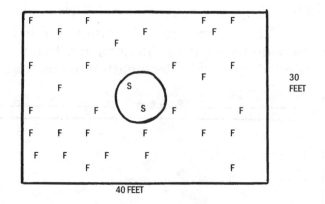

FROGS AND FLIES: Grades K to 3

1. One student is designated as the frog and squats in the center of the playing area.
2. The frog directs the flies to hop, skip, jump, etc., within the boundaries.
3. When the frog jumps to his feet, the flies run to the sidelines.
4. The flies tagged (flags pulled) by the frog before reaching the sidelines, become frogs and assist with the tagging.
5. The original frog continues giving all of the signals until a new game is started with a new frog in the center.
6. Play continues until four or five students remain untagged.

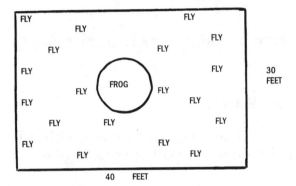

HIGH FIVE TAG: Grades K to 6

1. Five players are "it."
2. Free players freeze when tagged (or when flag is pulled) and put one hand high in the air.
3. Free players high-five frozen players to free them.
4. A player who steps outside of the boundaries is considered tagged.
5. Taggers are allowed a short time period to tag as many students as possible; after 10 to 20 seconds, stop and change taggers.

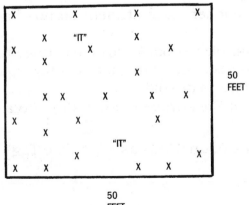

JACK FROST AND JANE THAW: Grades K to 6

1.   One or more students are chosen to be "Jack Frost" and carry a flag or a distinguishing object (tennis ball can, etc). If flags are used, all "Jacks" should carry the same color.
2.   One student is chosen to be "Jane Thaw" and carries a flag of a different color.
3.   The remainder of the class is scattered within the boundaries (flags may be worn).
4.   If "Jack Frost" tags a student (or pulls his flag), that student must freeze until "Jane Thaw" tags him. He may then "thaw out" and return to the game!

-Same boundaries as High Five Tag

PULL THE FLAG: Grades K to 6

1.   Each student has a flag. The class is scattered within the boundaries.
2.   The object is for each student to pull other's flags without his flag being pulled.
3.   Running out of bounds counts as having the flag pulled.
4.   There is no elimination. If a child's flag is pulled, he continues to pull other's flags!
5.   The game is stopped when only four or five students are still wearing flags.

-Same boundaries as High Five Tag

BACK TO BACK: Grades K to 6

1.   On command, students run (or use any specified locomotor movement) within the boundaries.
2.   On a signal from the teacher, each student stands back to back with one other student.
3.   Be creative! Other examples of body parts are: knee to knee, finger to finger, foot to foot, gastrocnemius to gastrocnemius, biceps to biceps, triceps to triceps, deltoid to deltoid.
4.   There is no elimination! Encourage students to find a different partner each time.

-Same boundaries as High Five Tag

MARCH ATTACK: Grades K to 6

1. Students are divided into two teams, X's and 0's; each team may wear a different colored flag.
2. The X's stand on one of the boundary lines with their backs to the playing area.
3. The 0's stand on the opposite boundary line, facing the playing area.
4. The 0's march forward on signal toward the X's.
5. On signal (whistle, tambourine, etc.), the X's turn around and chase the 0's back to their line.
6. Anyone who is tagged (or whose flag is pulled) changes teams.
7. The game is repeated--the teams exchanging roles.

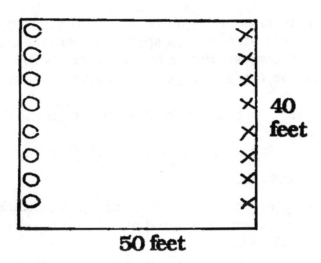

40 feet

50 feet

SUNDAY: Grades 3 to 6

1. Two parallel lines are marked about 50 feet apart.
2. One student is chosen to be "it" and stands in the area between the lines.
3. The remainder of the class stands on one of the lines (flags may be worn).
4. When the player in the middle shouts "Sunday!," all students immediately run to the other line.
5. The students who are tagged (flags are pulled), help "it" in the center.
6. False starts and not leaving as soon as "Sunday!" is shouted, are the same as being tagged (having the flag pulled).
7. Other days of the week may be called out to try and trick the class into false starting.
8. The game continues until four or five students remain untagged.

LOOSE CABOOSE: Grades 3 to 6

1.   Two or more students are selected to be a "loose caboose."
2.   The rest of the class forms trains of two students. To make a train, the student in back places his hands on the waist of the student immediately in front of him.
3.   The trains twist and turn to avoid being caught by a loose caboose.
4.   When a loose caboose attaches herself to the back of a train, the student in the front of that train becomes a new "loose caboose."
5.   To encourage maximal activity, it is suggested that one loose caboose is designated for every three trains.

-Same boundaries as High Five Tag

MUSCLE AND BONE TAG: Grades 3 to 6

1.   Two or more players are designated as "it." These taggers attempt to tag the other players in an awkward spot (knee, elbow, etc.) selected by the teacher. The "it" players carry a flag or other distinguishing object.
2.   A tagged player becomes a tagger. He is given the distinguishing object to carry.
3.   The other players must also hold their hands on the designated spot while being chased.

-Same boundaries as High Five Tag

LINE TAG: Grades 3 to 6

1.   All players are spread out on the lines of a basketball court.
2.   Two or more players are designated as "it" and carry flags (or other distinguishing objects).
3.   On a signal from the teacher, all students run only on the lines.
4.   If a player with a flag tags another player, she gives her flag to that player and the game continues.
5.   Variation: All students wear flags and are taggers -- if a student's flag is pulled, he continues to pull flags from other students!

-The lines of a basketball court may serve as boundaries.

SQUAD TAG: Grades 3 to 6

1.   One squad at a time is "it" (they may wear flags)
2.   The squad that is "it" has 15 seconds to tag as many students as possible.
3.   When a student is tagged, he marches in place and claps his hands.
4.   After 15 seconds, the teacher quickly counts the number of students tagged and gives the flags to another squad. A loud signal may be necessary to end the game. Tagging after the signal does not count.

-Same boundaries as High Five Tag-

CIRCLE HOOK-ON: Grades 3 to 6

1. Students are separated into groups of four. Three players join hands and form a circle; the fourth player is the tagger.
2. One of the three players in the circle wears a flag. The tagger's job is to pull that player's flag. The students in the circle attempt to protect the targeted player from the tagger. The tagger may not enter the circle to pull the flag. She must try to move around the outside of the circle.
3. Roles may be switched every 30 seconds or when the flag is pulled.

CROWS AND CRANES: Grades 3 to 6

1. Two teams stand facing each other, four feet apart. One team is named the "Crows," the other is named the "Cranes" (all students may wear flags).
2. When the teacher shouts "Crows," the Crows chase the Cranes back to their safe zone (a line marked 15 to 20 feet behind each team).
3. When the word "Cranes" is shouted, the Cranes chase the Crows.
4. A student who is tagged (flag is pulled) becomes a member of the tagging team.
5. The class may be tricked by using words like "crrrrrazy," "crrrrranberry," or "crrrrrown"! When the trick words are called, the students who move become members of the other team.
6. Alternate starting positions may be used (push-up, etc.).
7. Variation: Odds and Evens. One team is "Odd" and one team is "Even." The teacher calls out a number. If it is an odd number, the "Odd" team chases the "Even" team. If it is even, the 'Even" team becomes the chasers.

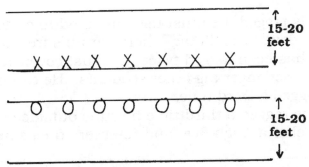

PURPLE AND WHITE: Grades 3 to 6

1. This game is played like Crows and Cranes except one team is "Purple" and one team is "White" (any variety of colors may be used).
2. A card with purple on one side and white on the other is tossed into the air.
3. When the card lands purple side up, the "Purple" team chases the "White" team. The "White" team chases when the card lands white side up.

-Same boundaries as Crows and Cranes

FLAG TAG: Grades 3 to 6

1. Each student has a flag. On a signal from the teacher the students attempt to pull each other's flags.
2. When a flag is pulled, the "puller" brings it to the teacher.
3. The person whose flag was pulled, goes to the teacher and retrieves her flag.
4. Variation: To return to the game the students must retrieve the flag from the teacher and perform an activity such as five jumping jacks or touch a boundary marker.

HOSPITAL TAG Grades 3-6

1. All students are "it."
2. The object is for students to tag each other and cause classmates to visit the "hospital!"
3. When a student is tagged, he must use one hand to cover up his new "injury." The student can still tag others with his free hand.
4. When a student has been tagged twice, he must cover up both "injuries" and can therefore no longer tag other students. He can only run and try to avoid being tagged a third time.
5. When a student is tagged a third time he runs outside of the boundaries and gives the teacher a "high five" and re-enters the game free of injuries!

RISK FACTOR TAG   Grades 3-6

1. Five students are "it" and carry flags which represent five of the risk factors for heart disease: Inactivity, Smoking, Obesity, Stress, and High Blood Pressure.
2. When a player who is "it" tags a free player, the "it" player calls out the name of his risk factor, i.e. smoking. The free player put one finger (representing one risk factor) in the air and continues running.
3. The second time a student is tagged he puts both two fingers in the air and continues running.
4. The third time a student is tagged he runs and does two laps around a cone representing the hospital. The student is now free of risk factors and continues playing the game.
5. After approximately 20-30 seconds, stop the game and have the players carrying flags give their flag to a classmate. Be sure the new "it" players know which risk factor they represent!

-Same boundaries as High Five Tag-

BARKER'S HOOPLA: Grades 3 to 6

1. Four to eight hoops are placed near the perimeter of an area approximately 30' by 30'.
2. Students are divided into four to eight teams.
3. Each team stands behind its own hoop filled with five or six beanbags (or plastic orange cones).
4. The object of the game is for each team member, by running around the outside of the hoops (no cutting corners!), to take beanbags one at a time from the hoops of the other teams, and place them in his own hoop.
5. Beanbags may not be thrown into the hoops; they must be placed inside the hoop.
6. When the stopping signal is given, players must freeze and release any beanbags in their hands. The teams count the number of beanbags in their hoops.

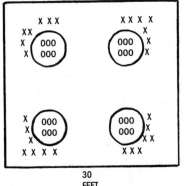

Summary

The games presented in this chapter are designed to keep all students actively participating for 80 to 90% of the game time so they have maximal opportunities to be active. The goal is for students to have fun and experience success and feelings of competence!

References

Carnes, C. (1990). *Awesome elementary school physical education activities.* Carmichael, CA: Education Company.

Pangrazi, R. (2007). *Dynamic physical education for elementary school children* (15th ed.). San Francisco, CA: Pearson Publishing.

Kasser, S. (1995) *Inclusive games.* Champaign, IL: Human Kinetics.

Lichtman, B. (1993) *Innovative games.* Champaign, IL: Human Kinetics.

Morris, D., & Stiehl, J. (1999). *Changing kids' games.* Reston, VA: NASPE.

Poppen, J., & Jacobsen, S. (1982). *Games that come alive!* Puyallup, WA: Action Productions.

Website

Center for Disease Control Activity Brochures
    http://www.cdc.gov/HealthyYouth/physicalactivity/brochures/pdf/teacher.PDF

Chapter 16
Assessment of Physical Fitness and Physical Activity

It is now known that a child may score well on fitness testing without being active. Conversely, children who are active but score poorly on fitness tests may lose confidence and develop negative attitudes toward physical activity. It is with this in mind that this chapter on assessment is written.

The purpose of physical fitness and physical activity assessment is to provide experiences through which students gain the knowledge and skills necessary to measure their own fitness and activity levels, interpret the results, and to plan and carry out their own fitness and activity programs. The ultimate goal of assessment experiences, is to empower and motivate students to adopt a physically active lifestyle. This chapter addresses the following topics related to assessment:

♥ Organization of assessment using the *FITNESSGRAM/ACTIVITYGRAM* battery
♥ Assessment of physical activity levels with *FITNESSGRAM/ACTIVITYGRAM*
♥ Interpretation of scores, motivation and recognition, and self-assessment
♥ Guidelines for providing fun, educational and empowering experiences

Assessment of Health Related Physical Fitness

Health related physical fitness assessment is conducted in a non-threatening environment. Mass "testing" is avoided; under no circumstances should students stand in long lines for fitness measurement. Negative attitudes toward physical activity are formed during fitness assessment during which a student is forced to perform in front of a large group of his peers. Circumstances under which fitness assessment is conducted may vary; the challenge is to organize evaluation so students are not injured or embarrassed. Any benefits which may be incurred from fitness measurement will be lost if a student is injured or humiliated in front of others.

A moderate warm-up combined with stretching activities is held at the start of each fitness measurement session for the purpose of preparing the body and specific muscles for use in each physical fitness item. For example, before students are measured on the back-saver sit and reach, students warm-up and stretch the hamstring muscles.

Body Composition, Muscular Strength and Endurance and Flexibility

Certain physical fitness items are best administered privately to students. Skinfolds, push-ups, curl-ups, trunk lift, and the back-saver sit-and-reach are the five recommended *FITNESSGRAM/ACTIVITYGRAM* items that can be assessed individually. Organization of these assessments may be different for the classroom teacher and the physical education specialist.

Organization of Assessment by the Classroom Teacher

The classroom teacher can set up a fitness measurement station in the back of the classroom blocked from the view of the class by a tumbling mat turned on its side, or other large object such as the teacher's desk. The teacher gives an assignment to the students on which they work independently. One student at a time is evaluated in the designated measurement area. It is suggested that one item is administered per day; performing these five activities consecutively on the same day may be too strenuous for some students. Individual measurement of students may take more time, but will prevent injury and the peer pressure and embarrassment that commonly occur during physical fitness appraisal.

Organization of Assessment by the Physical Education Specialist

A physical education specialist may organize her class so students participate in activity independently while she measures a few children at a time on a selected physical fitness item. Several stations are set up at which the students perform various activities on their own. Each station may involve the students using a different piece of equipment in non-stop activity; background music adds to the environment. One station is designated as the *"physical fitness measurement"* station.

Students rotate from station to station during the class period, working on their own until they reach the designated measurement station. Each day, at this station, the specialist evaluates each child on a different physical fitness item. For example, during one class period, all students are measured on the back-saver sit and reach upon rotation to the measurement station. During subsequent class periods, the curl-up, trunk lift, push-up and skinfold items may be measured in a similar manner.

Cardiovascular Fitness

The *FITNESSGRAM/ACTIVITYGRAM* manual includes two measures of cardiovascular fitness: the PACER (Progressive Aerobic Cardiovascular Endurance Run) and the one-mile run. The PACER is the recommended item. The one-mile run, although an optional item, is commonly used and is thus included here. Both the PACER and one-mile run are usually administered outdoors; however it may be possible to perform either one, especially the PACER, in a large indoor area. The classroom teacher and the specialist can use the same methods to administer the PACER or one-mile run.

Both the PACER and one-mile run can be administered to either half the class (in partners) or to the whole class at once with minimal risk of student embarrassment. The PACER has less risk for embarrassment as the less-fit students finish first and can continue walking laps as the more fit runners continue. This is in contrast to the one-mile run during which the fit students finish first, and then watch as the slower students finish last. Completing the one-mile run can be humiliating for the less fit students. When administering either of these items, teachers are encouraged to designate a cool-down area, away from the measurement area. As students finish, they proceed to the cool-down area where they can use hula hoops, jump ropes, flying discs, and other equipment.

The first time the PACER or one-mile run is administered, the class may be split up into partners. Each child has his own card on which his partner records his laps: either a PACER Lap Card (see the *FITNESSGRAM/ACTIVITYGRAM* Manual) or the One-Mile Run Lap Card (see Figure 16.1). Each time the runner completes one lap, his partner crosses off the appropriate lap number on the card. When the runner completes his final lap, his partner records either the total laps completed (PACER) or time (one-mile run). After half the class has completed the activity, the partners then switch roles; the recorder is now the runner.

Figure 16.1 One Mile Run Lap Card

Individual One Mile Run Lap Card

_____   _____
Name (first and last)   Room #

LAP #: 1   2   3   4   5   6   7   8   _____
(circle upon completion)   time   recorder

When administering the PACER or one-mile run for a second or third time to the same group of students, the whole class may run at once. Each student is responsible for keeping track of his laps and recording his score. One suggestion for the one-mile run is to give each student Popsicle sticks (one per lap to be run) prior to the start of the run. Students drop one stick at the start/finish line each time a lap is completed. As the final stick is dropped, the student listens for her time, called out by the teacher, and records it on her card. When administering the PACER to the entire class, the students call out the number of each lap out loud (after the beep) as they begin a new lap. When a student can no longer continue, he records the number of completed laps.

Assessment of Physical Activity

FITNESSGRAM/ACTIVITYGRAM includes the *ACTIVITYGRAM* Physical Activity Recall to assess each student's level of physical activity. The *ACTIVITYGRAM* assessment is a recall of the child's previous day's physical activity. In the assessment, the child is asked to report his activity levels for each 30-minute block of time during the previous day; both school and non-school days are assessed. This approach for measuring physical activity allows students to reflect on their own activity habits and understand the value of physical activity. Teachers are encouraged to use the recall form several times prior to the actual assessment to familiarize students with the format and terms.

Additionally, new research has begun to explore the reliability and validity of using pedometers to measure children's daily activity. The President's Council on Physical Fitness and Sports (www.fitness.org) has identified healthy levels of physical activity for girls and boys of 11,000 and 13,000 steps, respectively (www.president'schallenge.org).

Interpreting Assessment Results

Whereas the majority of past physical fitness tests have been based upon norm-referenced standards that are determined by comparing students to each other, *FITNESSGRAM/ACTIVITYGRAM* uses criterion-referenced standards to evaluate fitness performance. Criterion-referenced standards have been established to represent a level of fitness that offers some degree of protection against diseases that result from sedentary living. Performance is classified in two general areas: "Needs Improvement" and "Healthy Fitness Zone (HFZ)." *FITNESSGRAM/ACTIVITYGRAM* contains tables that identify the HFZ for each test based upon students' gender and age.

Self-Assessment

Once students have experienced the process of fitness assessment under the teacher's supervision, the teacher provides opportunities for self-assessment. Students are given the responsibility, in a non-competitive atmosphere, to measure their own fitness, interpret their scores, and set personal goals. *FITNESSGRAM/ACTIVITYGRAM* provides specific information on conducting student self-assessments.

Recognition and Motivation

FITNESSGRAM/ACTIVITYGRAM includes a recognition program called *You Stay Active* that encourages youth to make regular physical activity an integral part of their lives. The recognition program rewards participation and deemphasizes the "everyone must be or get fit" philosophy. The new philosophy is that "everyone should be or get physically active." *You Stay Active* not only rewards more children for participation, but correlates with the Surgeon General's findings about the importance of physical activity.

Assessment Guidelines

♥ **Avoid using the word "test" (as in physical fitness "test").** Use words such as "measurement," "evaluation," "appraisal," or "assessment" instead of the word "test." Many times students have negative attitudes toward "test"-taking; they tend to react more positively when the teacher uses alternate words. The statement, "Today, class, we will measure how strong your heart and lungs are by running the PACER," is less threatening than, "Today, class, you will be tested on the PACER."

♥ **Make fitness evaluation a learning experience.** Teach students why their fitness is being evaluated. For example, the teacher might say, "Today we will be doing the back-saver sit and reach. We will be measuring the flexibility of our hamstring muscles. It is important to be flexible in our hamstrings so we can be physically active and prevent soreness and injury."

♥ **Provide physical fitness assessment activities in all grade levels.** Begin assessment experiences in kindergarten. At this level, emphasize teaching young children concepts such as, "The heart is as big as the fist," and "The heart beats faster when we move our bodies." The PACER is the physical fitness item that relates to these concepts. However, kindergarten and first grade students probably cannot last more than one or two laps on the PACER. Accordingly, the 20-meter PACER distance can be modified to five meters; this will allow the students to become comfortable with the PACER cadence and with running and walking for a continuous amount of time. The following statement is appropriate for kindergarten and first grade students.

> Today class, we are going to run the PACER. Each of us will run back and forth between these two lines. When the voice says to start, run across to the other line like I am showing you. Once we reach the other line, we will stop and wait for a beep to sound on the tape. When we hear the beep, we run back to the first line like this. The object is not to run our fastest, but to run at a comfortable speed. The beeps on the tape will start to get faster. If we get tired, let's try to walk fast and pump our arms. If you don't know what to do, watch me.

♥ **Conduct fitness evaluation at the beginning, middle, and at the end of the school year.** Provide opportunities for self-measurement throughout the year. At the beginning of the school year, students participate in four to six weeks of conditioning activities before fitness levels are measured. Provide each student with an individual card on which he can record his own scores. Figure 16.2 contains an example of an individualized physical fitness card with space for three assessment dates for the six recommended *FITNESSGRAM/ACTIVITYGRAM* items. The following statement may be made to students: "Today I have set up physical fitness stations; rotate to each station and see if you can break your own physical fitness records."

Figure 16.2 Individual Health Related Fitness Record Card

INDIVIDUAL HEALTH RELATED PHYSICAL FITNESS RECORD

Name: _____   D.O.B.: __/__/__   Teacher: _____
         Last   First

FITNESSGRAM Items	Fall Date___ Age___		Self-Assessment Date___ Age___		Spring Date___ Age___	
	Score	HFZ	Score	HFZ	Score	HFZ
Height and Weight	H W	H W	H W	H W	H W	H W
Back Saver Sit and Reach* (nearest inch) Hamstring Flexibility	R L	R L	R L	R L	R L	R L
Curl-Up** (# correct) Abdominal Strength and Endurance						
Push-Up (# correct) Upper Body Strength and Endurance						
Trunk Lift*(nearest inch) Trunk Extensor Strength and Flexibility						
PACER (complete laps) Cardiovascular Fitness						
Skinfolds (mm) **or BMI** (www.cdc.gov for BMI calculation)						

* The maximum score recorded on both of these items is 12.

**The maximum score on curl-ups is 75

♥ **Encourage students to score within the Healthy Fitness Zone on each test.** Teach students about the Healthy Fitness Zones and inform them of the HFZ for their age and gender. Encourage students to set fitness and activity goals that will help them to attain scores within their zone.

♥ **Emphasize self-improvement over class competition.** Establish a non-competitive atmosphere. The following statement clarifies this point: "It's not important to compare your scores with those of other students. What is important is your individual score and how you progress throughout the year. Try to score within your Healthy Fitness Zone."

♥ **Provide students with feedback about their scores on each item.** Assist students in interpreting each of their scores.

♥ **Allow students to set personal goals.** Recognize each child's personal fitness and activity level and encourage her to set individual goals that are within her reach. Fitness goals may focus on achieving the Healthy Fitness Zones or on participating in physical activity outside the school setting. *FITNESSGRAM/ACTIVITYGRAM* includes goal-setting forms.

♥ **Assign grades based on student effort, not upon physical fitness scores.** Give students the responsibility for grading themselves in physical education. Emphasize effort, participation and self-improvement. One section of a sample Self-Grading Form is shown in Figure 16.3. Directions to the class are:

> It is most important in physical education that each of you do the best that you can. It is not important to me that one of you can do more curl-ups than someone else. What is important is that each of you tries to do your best and achieve a health level of fitness. Your grades in physical education are based upon how hard you try--not on how good you are at a skill or physical fitness. There is really only one person who knows how hard you try. Who do you think that person is? That is right--YOU are the one who knows. For that reason, I am asking each of you to give yourself a grade in physical education for the last nine weeks. Please write in the grade you feel you deserve, your reasons, and sign your name. If I disagree with the grade that you give yourself, I will discuss it with you. You have five minutes to think about this and fill in the information. I will come around to help any of you who have questions.

Figure 16.3 Physical Education Self-Grading Form

PHYSICAL EDUCATION SELF-GRADING FORM

Name _____   Room # _____

♥♥♥♥♥♥♥♥♥♥♥♥♥♥♥♥♥♥♥ First Grading Period ♥♥♥♥♥♥♥♥♥♥♥♥♥♥♥♥♥♥♥♥♥♥

I deserve the grade of _____.

My reasons are: _____

_____

_____

Student's signature _____

♥ **De-emphasize extrinsic rewards such as badges, ribbons, certificates, and food.** Avoid using extrinsic rewards. Extrinsic rewards such as badges sometimes become the sole motivating force; when these rewards are taken away, the motivation is gone. Developing positive activity and fitness habits can be compared to brushing teeth. We brush our teeth to keep them strong and healthy. Nobody receives a badge for having healthy teeth (maybe a free toothbrush once in a while!). The reward is that our teeth last a lifetime. Similarly, children (and adults) need to regularly participate in physical activity to be healthy. A lifetime of health and vigor is the best reward one can receive!

♥ **Teach mental toughness.** Teach students the difference between initial fatigue, and pain that may result in injury. Encourage students to "keep going;" however, instruct them to stop if they experience pain. "Mental Toughness" means to continue exercising past the first signs of tiring.

Summary

When handled wisely, assessment of physical fitness and physical activity can be an enjoyable, empowering learning experience for children. Emphasis is placed upon individual progress, not on competition among students or instructors. The ultimate goals of fitness evaluation are to give students the knowledge and skills to self-evaluate and to empower them to take responsibility for making regular physical activity a part of their lives outside the school setting.

References

American Alliance for Health, Physical Education, Recreation and Dance (AAHPERD). (1996). *Physical Best and children with disabilities.* Reston VA: AAHPERD.

Fox, K.R., & Biddle, S.J. (1988). The use of fitness tests: Educational and psychological considerations. *Journal of Physical Education, Recreation, and Dance (JOPERD), 59*(2), 47-53.

Cooper Institute for Aerobics Research. (2005). *FITNESSGRAM/ACTIVITYGRAM test administration manual (3rd ed.).* Champaign, IL: Human Kinetics.

Corbin, C.B., Lovejoy, P.Y., Steingard, P., & Emerson, R. (1990). Fitness awards: Do they accomplish their intended objectives? *American Journal of Health Promotion, 4,* 345-351.

East, W., Frazier, J., & Matney, L. (1989). Assessing the physical fitness of elementary school children--Using community resources. *JOPERD, 60*(6), 54-56.

Holt/Hale, S. (1997). Assessment Series. Assessing and improving fitness in elementary physical education. Reston, VA: NASPE.

Jenkins, D., & Staub, J. (1985). Student fitness--The physical educator's role. *JOPERD, 56*(7), 31-32.

Johnson, R., & Lavay, B. (1989). Fitness testing for children with special needs. *JOPERD, 60*(6), 50-53.

Lacy, E., & Marshall, B. (1984). *FITNESSGRAM:* An answer to physical fitness improvement for school children. *JOPERD, 55*(1), 18-19.

Le Masurier, G., Beighle, A., Corbin, C., Darst, P., Morgan, C., Pangrazi, R., Wilde, B. & Vincent, S. Pedometer-determined physical activity levels of youth. *Journal of Physical Activity and Health,* Vol. 2 (No. 2), April, 2005, pp. 159-168.

McSwegin, P. (1989). Assessing physical fitness. *JOPERD, 60*(6), 33.

McSwegin, P.J., Pemberton, C., & Petray, C. (1989). Fitting in fitness: An educational plan, *JOPERD. 60*(1), 32-34.

Parker, M., & Pemberton, C. (1989). Elementary classroom teachers: Untapped resources for fitness assessment. *JOPERD, 60*(6), 61-63.

Pemberton, C., & McSwegin, P. (1989). Fitting in fitness: Goal setting and motivation. *JOPERD, 60*(1), 39-41.

Petray, C. (1989). Organizing physical fitness assessment (Grades K-6)--Strategies for the elementary physical education specialist. *JOPERD, 60*(6), 57-60.

Petray, C., Blazer, S., Lavay, B., & Leeds, M. (1989). Fitting in fitness: Designing the fitness testing environment. *JOPERD, 60*(1), 35-38.

President's Council on Physical Fitness and Sports. (2005). *The Presidential Fitness Award program.* Washington, D.C.: author.

Schiemer, S. (1996). The pacer – a really fun run. In *Ideas for Action II: More Award Winning Approaches to Physical Activity.* Reston, VA: AAHPERD.

Seaman, J. (1995). (Ed.). *Physical BEST and individuals with disabilities.* Reston VA: AAHPERD.

Stroot, S., & Baumgartner, S. (1989). Fitness assessment: Putting computers to work. *JOPERD, 60*(6), 44-49.

Whitehead, J. (1989). Fitness assessment results--Some concepts and analogies. *JOPERD, 60*(6), 39-43.

Websites

President's Council on Physical Fitness and Sports (PCPFS) www.fitness.org

PCPFC Awards Program www.president'schallenge.org

PART FIVE

Beyond the Classroom!

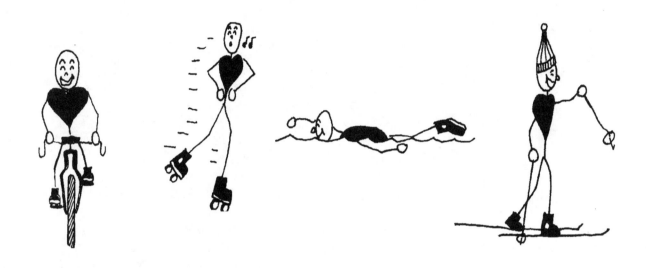

Chapter 17, "Integrating Concepts Across the Curriculum," includes practical ideas for integrating physical activity and fitness concepts into the physical education classroom and throughout the school setting.

Chapter 18, **"Promoting Physical Activity and Fitness in the Home and Community,"** presents ideas for promoting physically active lifestyles outside of school. These include: newsletters, letters to parents, mall demonstrations, National Physical Fitness and Sports Month celebrations, parent nights, news releases, fun runs, jog-a-thons and physical activity booklets. Websites containing ideas for physical activity promotion are provided.

Chapter 17
Integrating Concepts Across the Curriculum

Concepts pertaining to health related physical fitness and physical activity may be incorporated not only into the physical education lesson, but into the total school curriculum. This chapter provides ideas for introducing and reinforcing concepts in physical education and throughout the school.

Teaching Physical Fitness and Activity Concepts in the Physical Education Class

There are numerous approaches for incorporating concepts into the physical education lesson. The following are examples of how the teacher can teach and reinforce physical activity and fitness knowledge.

1. **Introduce Concepts During Activity.** Teach concepts that apply directly to the activity in which students are participating. For example, during a rope jumping activity, students drop their ropes and feel their pulse. During activities held early in the year, students learn that there are several locations at which the pulse can be felt. Later on in the year, students learn how to calculate their maximum and target heart rates.

2. **Plan and Teach Lessons According to the FITT Guidelines and Principles of Exercise.** Explain the FITT guidelines and principles of exercise and allow students to see the results of their implementation.

3. **Allow Opportunities for Pre-, Post-, and Self-Assessment in Physical Fitness and Activity.** Emphasize the fitness *process*. Fitness and activity assessment is a learning experience; the *process* of learning how to assess one's fitness and activity is more important than the *product* of fitness scores. Explain healthy levels of fitness and activity, lifetime health benefits, and how fitness and activity are assessed, achieved and maintained (Chapter 3). Students can use an individual physical fitness record card to monitor their individual progress and set goals (Chapter 16).

4. **Assign Homework Related to Physical Activity and Fitness.** Use *FITNESSGRAM/ACTIVITYGRAM* activity logs for recording activity outside the classroom. Assign written reports on physical activity and fitness.

5. **Conduct Class Discussions of Current Events Related to Physical Fitness.** Ask students to bring in articles related to physical fitness from newspapers and magazines. Assign oral reports or hold class discussions related to the articles.

6. **Use Learning Materials from Organizations such as the American Heart Association and the National Dairy Council.** Acquire films and materials to reinforce concepts. (www.americanheart.org and www.nationaldairycouncil.org/NationalDairyCouncil/)

7. **Invite Members of the Local Community to Speak to the Class.** Invite doctors, nurses, and other health care professionals to speak to the class on topics related to physical activity and fitness.

Teaching Physical Fitness and Activity Concepts Across the Curriculum

Physical activity and fitness concepts are related to many subjects in the school curriculum. The following approaches may be used to reinforce concepts throughout the school setting. Encourage student ideas!

1. **Create Bulletin Boards in the Gymnasium, Cafeteria, Multipurpose Room, Library, or Classroom to Illustrate Concepts.** Students design bulletin boards. Sample themes for bulletin boards are:

    a. **"Move It Or Lose It!"** Combine drawings or photos of people participating in physical activity with paragraphs written by the students about their favorite activities.

    b. **"You Can't Drown in Sweat!"** Draw or find pictures of people involved in physical activity. Present sweating as a valuable body function with a positive connotation.

    c. **"Muscle of the Month."** Highlight one major muscle each month. Include pictures of the muscle, its location, its function, and how it can be strengthened. Include this muscle in science lessons (how it functions), and in spelling (correct spelling).

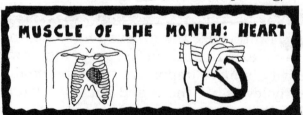

2. **Integrate Concepts Into Other Subjects of the School Curriculum.** The following are examples how concepts can be integrated into other subject areas such as math, language arts, science and health.

    a. **Math**
      ♥   Calculate personal BMI (Chapter 3 – Figure 3.4)
      ♥   Calculate maximum heart rate, target heart rate range, and the 10-second target heart rate range (Chapter 11).

♥ Students take pulse for one minute and use that information to calculate the approximate number of times their heart beats in one hour, one day, and one year (Figure 17.1).

Figure 17.1 Calculating daily, hourly, and yearly heart rates

80 BEATS PER MINUTE
equals
4,800 BEATS PER HOUR
equals
115,200 BEATS PER DAY
equals
42,048,000 BEATS PER YEAR!

♥ Calculate distance covered using a pedometer (Chapter 11). Students use pedometers, determine number of steps taken, and use personal stride length to calculate distance. Figure 17.2 shows the calculation for a student with a stride length of 2.0 feet who has taken 3,000 steps.

Figure 17.2 Calculating distance covered in miles

Step 1 3,000 (steps)

$\quad\quad\quad\dfrac{\times\ 2.0'\ \text{(stride length)}}{6,000\ \text{(feet traveled)}}$

Step 2 6,000 steps/5,280 feet in one mile

Distance traveled: *1.13 miles*

b. **Language Arts.** Integrate key terminology used in the physical education lesson into spelling lists (Figure 17.3).

Figure 17.3 Physical activity and fitness terminology

Sample Spelling Words

a. heart	e. blood	i. active	m. muscle	q. pedometer
b. lungs	f. pulse	j. strength	n. cardiovascular	r. stride
c. artery	g. stretch	k. endurance	o. body composition	s. calorie
d. vein	h. flexibility	l. oxygen	p. capillary	t. energy

c. **Science**

♥ Dissect a lamb or beef heart.

♥ Experiment with the effects of exercise on the heart. Monitor heart rates and blood pressures while engaging in physical activities of varying intensities

♥ Teach the names and actions of the muscles (See Appendix B for location of muscles).

d. **Health**

♥ Plan discussions of health related physical fitness components to coincide with fitness assessment.

♥ Students determine their own risk for type 2 diabetes at www.diabetes.org/diabetesphd/default.jsp?WTLPromo=HOME_P HD&vms=200763452712 (Diabetes PHD)

♥ Students determine individual nutrition guidelines at www.mypyramid.gov.

♥ Students bring in and compare nutrition labels of their favorite foods

3. **Order Books Related to Physical Activity and Fitness Through the Librarian.** Assign oral or written book reports. Establish a physical activity and fitness area in the library.

4. **Arrange Field Trips to Local Universities, Hospitals and the Supermarket.** Arrange for students to visit the exercise physiology laboratory at a university or the cardiac rehabilitation center in a hospital. Students can visit a local supermarket to learn about placement of foods within the store and on the shelves, as well as to read and compare a wide variety of nutrition labels.

Summary

A person's health and fitness affect all aspects of his life; it is difficult to separate the concepts pertaining to health related fitness and physical activity from other school subjects. Teaching concepts on a school-wide basis will enhance student learning and increase the focus on the value of a physically active lifestyle!

References

Bannister, S., & Harlow, C. (1997). Integrating math and writing skills into the physical education curriculum. *Teaching Elementary Physical Education, 8*(8), 28-29.

Pate, R. (1985). Teaching physical fitness concepts in public schools. In *Implementation of health fitness exercise programs*, D. Cundiff (Ed.). Reston, VA: AAHPERD.

Petray, C., & Cortese, P. (1988). Physical fitness: A vital component of the school health curriculum. *Health Education, 19*(5), 4-7.

Sander, A.N., & Burton, E.C. (1989). Learning aids -- Enhancing fitness knowledge in elementary physical education. *Journal of Physical Education, Recreation and Dance, 60*(1), 56-59.

Websites

American Diabetes Association – a test for type 2 diabetes risk
    www.diabetes.org/diabetesphd/default.jsp?WTLPromo=HOME_PHD&vms=200763452712
American Heart Association (AHA) www.americanheart.org
AHA Online Resources for Teachers
    www.americanheart.org/presenter.jhtml?identifier=3003357
Center for Disease Control and Prevention-Ideas for physical activity and nutrition
    www.bam.gov and
    http://www.cdc.gov/HealthyYouth/physicalactivity/brochures/pdf/teacher.PDF
Ideas for the classroom teacher www.take10.net/whatistake10.asp?page=new
National Dairy Council www.nationaldairycouncil.org/NationalDairyCouncil
Physical Education lesson ideas www.pecentral.org/lessonideas/pelessonplans.html

Chapter 18
Promoting Physical Activity and Fitness in the Home and Community

The physical education program provides the educational experiences through which students acquire the knowledge, attitudes and skills necessary to develop healthy levels of fitness and lifetime activity habits. However, the promotion of physical activity and fitness must extend beyond the school setting if students are to be successful in adopting an active lifestyle. This chapter presents ideas for promoting physically active lifestyles outside of school setting.

1. **Newsletters.** Develop monthly newsletters than contain articles written by both teachers and students. "FITNEWS" is an example of a title for a monthly newsletter written by both teachers and students about class activities related to physical fitness and physical activity. It can also include nutrition-related topics such as healthy snack ideas, bringing healthy food to parties and reading nutrition-facts labels.

2. **Letters to parents.** Send letters to parents (see Chapter 7) and members of the school board to educate the community about the importance of regular participation in physical activity. Examples of school physical education activities can also be included.

3. **Mall demonstrations.** Conduct a demonstration of physical education activities in a mall or shopping center to publicize the physical education program. American Education Week, usually held in October, is an appropriate time for such a demonstration as public awareness of the schools is emphasized during this week.

4. **National Physical Fitness and Sports Month celebration.** Each year in May, schools throughout the nation organize special activities to promote healthy physical activity habits and nutrition choices. Ask both parents and students to visit websites (www.americaonthemove.org , www.fitness.gov/ and www.aahperd.org/NASPE/) to develop ideas. One idea is to promote a school and community-wide effort to cut down on television viewing (www.tvturnoff.org/facts.htm). Possibilities are endless!

5. **Parent nights.**
   ♥ Organize a physical activity and fitness demonstration to educate parents and to demonstrate activities from the physical education program. It can be held during the evening in a local junior high or high school gymnasium. With the assistance of other teachers and parent volunteers, a "**3 RING CIRCUS**" can be presented; three different activities are demonstrated at one time!

   ♥ Back to School Night and Open House provide an excellent opportunity for a physical fitness demonstration or display.

6. **News releases.** Send in articles about newsworthy achievements in physical activity and fitness to the local newspapers. For example, at the completion of fitness assessment, a headline might read, "Elliott Elementary School Students Run 300 Miles!" The article proceeds to describe how the one-mile run was completed by 300 students!

7. **Fun runs.** Invite parents and members of the community to walk and jog along with the students in a one, two, or three mile run around the perimeter of the school.

8. **Special events.** Hold special events that bring the community into the school. For example, organize and conduct a Jog-A-thon. Jog-a-Thons are one method of promoting physical activity among the students, faculty, and community. Additionally, Jog-a-thons are an effective method for raising funds the program. Figure 18.1 provides guidelines for organizing a Jog-A-Thon.

9. **Physical activity and fitness booklets.** Create a physical activity and fitness booklet emphasizing the importance of physical activity for children. This type of booklet increases public awareness of the need for structured physical education programs in the elementary schools and provides parents and guardians with suggestions for helping to improve their child's participation in physical activity. A sample booklet is shown in Figure 18.3.

Figure 18.1 Step-by-step procedures for organizing and conducting a jog-a-thon

HOW TO "RUN" A JOG-A-THON!

1. Communicate with the principal to obtain the permission necessary from the district and the school to conduct a fund-raising event.

2. Communicate with the principal, secretaries, faculty, and the P.T.A. in setting a date and time for the event. Publicize the event in the physical education newsletter, in the school bulletin, and through the P.T.A.

3. Meet with the students and teachers to explain the Jog-a-Thon procedures. Some procedural considerations might be:
    ♥   The purpose of the Jog-a-Thon, and how the money will be used, is explained to students.
    ♥   The Jog-a-Thon will last for a specific amount of time (30 to 40 minutes).
    ♥   The students ask for pledges of a specified amount of money for their participation in the event rather than pledges per lap or per mile. This procedure reduces record keeping.
    ♥   Students are instructed to ask adults, not peers, for pledges.

4. Send home a letter to parents, with a permission slip included, explaining the procedures for the Jog-a-Thon and inviting the parents to attend. A sample letter is shown in Figure 18.2.

Figure 18.1 Step-by-step procedures for organizing and conducting a jog-a-thon (continued)

5. Inform local newspapers and local television news stations of the event. Send a follow-up letter inviting them to attend the Jog-a-Thon.

6. Guest joggers, such as policemen, firemen, city officials, school board members, local college students, and athletes, may be invited.

7. Encourage teachers and guests to jog along with the students!

8. Establish committees involving students from each classroom. One student per class is in charge of distributing the individual pledge sheets that include spaces for names, addresses, phone numbers, and the amount of money pledged. A second student is in charge of a "class pledge sheet" She keeps a daily record of the total class pledges. A third student per class assists the classroom teacher with the collection of pledge money.

Class Pledge Sheet

NAME	ADDRESS	PHONE	PLEDGE
Holly Bennett	123 Arm Circle	847-2339	$5.00
Sierah Bennett	456 Boat Road	846-1882	$1.00
Bette Walker	789 Tennis Court	847-6845	$3.00

Total Class Pledges

9. Print large nametags for students similar to the numbers worn by runners in 5 and 10 Kilometer races. Instead of individual numbers, the tags might include the classroom number and the title of the event-- "Jog-A-Thon, 2001." "Special guest" tags, similar to the tags the students wear, are made for visitors. Safety pins are used to attach the tags to the shirts.

10. Mark a large oval or circular course using cones and chalk (the type used to line baseball fields).

11. Use a bullhorn or microphone to communicate with participants prior to, and during the Jog-A-Thon.

12. Remind students, at the conclusion of the Jog-A-Thon, to collect pledges within a specified time period. One week is suggested.

13. When the new equipment arrives, invite parents to a physical fitness demonstration at which the new equipment will be highlighted.

Figure 18.2 Sample letter to parents

May 1, 2008

Dear Parents:

Our physical education program is experiencing a very ACTIVE year. Our next major activity will be a **Jog-a-Thon** on May 18th, 2008. The major purpose of the **Jog-a-Thon** is to promote physical activity not only school-wide, but also in the community.

Another purpose of the **Jog-a-Thon** is to raise money for the physical education program. With a successful fund-raising effort, our school will be able to purchase the supplies necessary to keep our physical education program going strong!

Your entire family is invited to participate in the **Jog-a-Thon.** You are invited to come join us and walk or jog along with the students at 2:00 P.M. on May 18th. Many of the classroom teachers, the principal, school board members, members of the city council, along with physical education majors from California State University, Long Beach, will be walking and jogging with the Elliott students.

I will be meeting with each classroom to discuss the procedures for obtaining sponsors and collecting pledges. Raising money during the **Jog-a-Thon** is not mandatory; the focus is on having fun being physically active together as a school and community.

It should prove to be a FUN and ACTIVE afternoon for everyone! If you have any questions, please call the school and leave a message for me. Thank you for your support.

Sincerely,

Mrs. Hylin Neese

Mrs. Hylin Neese
Elliott Elementary School
Physical Education Specialist

♥ ♥

Please return this portion to the teacher by May 11, 2008.

_____ has permission to take part in the
student's name (please print)

Jog-A-Thon on Friday, May 18, 2008 at 2:00 P.M.

_____   **Room #** _____
parent/guardian signature

Figure 18.3 Physical activity and fitness booklet for parents and guardians

Physical Activity and Fitness

For Young Children

and Parents and Guardians of Young Children

TABLE OF CONTENTS